How To
Install and Finish
Synthetic Aircraft Fabrics

Other TAB books by the author:

How To Install and Finish Synthetic Aircraft Fabrics

By Joe Christy

MODERN AVIATION SERIES

TAB BOOKS

BLUE RIDGE SUMMIT, PA. 17214

FIRST EDITION

FIRST PRINTING—FEBRUARY 1979

Library of Congress Cataloging in Publication Data

Christy, Joe.
  How to install & finish synthetic aircraft fabrics.

  Includes index.
    1. Airplanes—Fabrics. I. Title.
TL699.F2C45   629.134'2   78-20972
ISBN 0-8306-9828-0
ISBN 0-8306-2252-7 pbk.

Cover courtesy of *The AOPA Pilot.*

Contents

Chapter 1
Poly-Fiber, Ceconite,
Razorback, & Eonnex

The best possible exterior covering for aircraft structures is determined by the kind of aircraft to be covered and, of course, whatever happens to be available (and economically feasible) for that purpose at a given time. According to a 1909 issue of FLIGHT magazine, the Wright Model A biplane had wings "...covered with an upper and lower sheet of gray cloth placed diagonally. This is nailed to the frame. The cloth, which is not varnished, is quite slack in dry weather, although said to become tight in damp. It is dirty and oil splattered."

That same year, the French-built Antionette monoplane had wings covered with Michelin "rubber-proofed" fabric.

By 1913, young Matty Laird's first airplane was covered with unbleached muslin treated with a mixture of hide glue, water, and formaldehyde, boiled, and applied while hot.

But in 1914 the French developed cellulose-nitrate dope, and this, applied to Irish linen or cotton fabric, become the standard treatment for fabric-covered airplanes until after WW-II.

Nitrate dope effectively protected cotton fabric for up to ten years when properly applied and maintained, although it was highly flammable. It provided less than the ideal finish due to its combustible nature, but since it tautened the fabric for a smooth exterior surface, properly filled the fabric weave for good protection, and was reasonably priced (about $2 per gallon), it stayed with us for a long time.

Nitrate dope is still useful, though seldom anymore as a final finish on fabric covered aircraft. Quite a bit of cotton (Grade A long staple, meeting TSO-C-15 requirements, tensile strength of 80 lbs per inch, both warp and fill) is still used for covering, although nowadays it is usually finished with butyrate dope.

After WW-II, a whole generation of pilots was conditioned for something better than the cotton-nitrate dope combination, partly at least as a result of unhappy experiences with the large amount of war surplus dope and fabric—much of which had deteriorated due to age and improper storage—and which was often applied by people uninstructed in this art.

The "something better" was the synthetics, but the right combinations of cloth and finish required the test of time to sort out.

Today, there are only two basic types of synthetic fabric material available for the exterior covering of aircraft structures: Fiberglas, which is tautened (to a degree) with aircraft dope, usually butyrate; and the heat-shrinkable cloths which need only to be coated for protection such as Orlon, Nylon, and Dacron. Orlon and Nylon (an acrylic and a polyamide, respectively), are not satisfactory for aircraft exterior covering because of rapid deterioration or excessive elasticity. So, after many combinations of fabrics and finishes were tried, the fabrics that have proven superior to all others are Fiberglas and Dacron—properly applied and finished.

The most popular synthetic cloth for exterior aircraft covering today is the polyester known as griege Dacron, which is marketed under several trade names such as Stits Poly-Fiber and Ceconite. Another is "Eonnex," a Dacron cloth treated with modified epoxy resins.

The Dacron cloth styles vary. Ceconite has more threads per sq/in in one direction than in another; while Stits Poly-Fiber is a "square weave," possessing an equal number of threads in both directions. Both Ceconite and Poly-Fiber are available in several different weights.

Normally, Dacron is cleaned and heat-shrunk after it is woven; but for aircraft covering it is left in its raw, unfinished state, a "greige" fabric, and its 10% shrinkability (through the application of heat) remains, allowing one to achieve a neat, wrinkle-free airplane cover job with a minimum of labor.

Applying finish to Dacron is really where you have to get your act together. Dacron is manufactured by the condensation of Dimethyl terephatalate and ethylene glycol. It is a very smooth monofilament, and has no microscopic surface texture on which conventional coatings can attach for better adhesion, as with the organic fibers, cotton and linen. So it is in the finishing process where success or failure—and a range of semi-successes or semi-failures in between—occurs in most airplane covering jobs.

Grade A cotton fabric covered the 1929 Travel Airs produced by Walter Beech. Airplanes are still being covered with cotton today. Beech Aircraft Corporation Photo.

Stits Poly-Fiber

As Ray Stits explains, before the polyester (Dacron) thread can be woven into a fabric it must be lubricated for processing through the looms. The lubricating oil accounts for approximately 2/10ths of 01% of the total weight of Dacron fabric. Diethylene glycol is one of the conditioning and lubricating agents used by the mills. The raw Dacron also picks up considerable oil drippings from loom machinery. The smooth surface and presence of a lubricant are two of the reasons for the poor adhesion of nitrate and butyrate dope on Dacron greige.

The adhesion of nitrate dope on Dacron was tested by the people at Stits Aircraft (one of the pioneers in synthetic fabrics for aircraft use), and they report that a 90-degree peel test on a two-inch finishing tape, using a small weight-measuring scale, will show that nitrate dope on Dacron has a peel resistance of one to four pounds, depending upon the dope application technique. Butyrate applied to raw Dacron will have a peel resistance of one pound or less.

We have learned from experience that butyrate dope continues to tauten fabric with age, and heavy finish coats on heat-shrunk

Dacron may eventually distort the airframe. You can guard against this condition to a degree by using the "non-tautening" butyrate dope containing additional amounts of plasticizers (triphenyl phosphate and tricresyl phosphate), but the plasticizers lose effectiveness after a few years in a hot sun. Therefore, Stits contends that nitrate and butyrate should not be used on Dacron, and that, for a lasting finish that won't further tauten Dacron with age, one must use the Stits resin compounds, "Poly-Brush" and "Poly-Spray" to fill the weave and provide protection from the sun, while giving a good base for the final finish coats.

Evidence of how well regarded the Stits' system is turns up in the used plane market with some regularity when, as a sales gimmick, a fabric covered aircraft is represented as having been re-covered and finished with the Stits Poly-Fiber Process when in fact the finish is synthetic enamel. (Stits advises that a short soak test with MEK will swell and wrinkle synthetic enamel, while Stits Poly-Tone merely softens.)

We must admit that we don't report so favorably on a commercial product without some trepidation. But, dammit, we're obligated to tell it like it is.

The peel resistance of a two-inch finishing tape applied with Poly-Brush on Stits Dacron (Poly-Fiber) is seven to nine pounds—more than twice that of nitrate—so the all-important adhesion properties of this finishing system can't be ignored. The Stits Poly-Dope coatings cut through the oil coating on the Dacron fibers to achieve this adhesion, according to Stits.

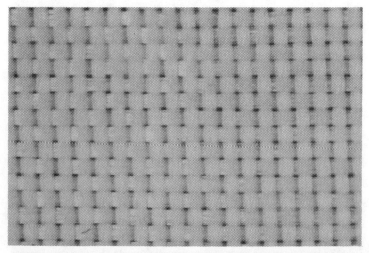

Stits Poly-Fiber (magnified 30 times) is a Dacron formula with untwisted threads and a square weave.

The flexibility of the non-tautening Poly-Dope coatings allow the loads to be carried by the heat-tautened fabric, instead of by the finish as it is with other methods. The Stits finishing process will not support combustion. It consists of two coats of Poly-Brush and three to six coats of Poly-Spray prior to the color coats. The final color coats—three are recommended—may be Stits Poly-Tone paint or Aero-Thane, a polyurethane enamel.

There is no appreciable difference in the "finished-out" weights of the heaviest Dacrons (whether Poly-Fiber or Ceconite), Fiberglas, and Grade A cotton. Grade A cotton weighs 4 oz sq yd.

The Stits square-weave Poly-Fiber is offered in three weights:

Style D-101A 3.7 oz sq yd; average strength, 130 lbs per inch width. Thread count, 53 × 53.

Style D-103 2.7 oz sq yd; average strength, 95 lbs per inch width. A fine weave, 15 lbs stronger than Grade A cotton; provides a minimum weight and very smooth finish.

Style D-104 1.7 oz sq yd; average strength, 60 lbs per inch width. A very fine weave used over plywood surfaces.

Ceconite

Ceconite Dacron cloth is also offered in three weights, and although Ceconite is not a square weave—its thread-count is 49 × 58—and it is woven with twisted thread instead of the flat, smooth thread in Poly-Fiber, its average tensile strength is about the same.

Perhaps one reason for the popularity of the Ceconite Process is that it uses nitrate and butyrate dopes, and aircraft mechanics with a background in dope/fabric work are experienced in the use of such finishes.

The Ceconite finish procedure is essentially the same as that used on Grade A cotton or Irish linen. And since nitrate dope has much better adhesive qualities than buytrate, the prime, and two base coats are nitrate, followed by three to four coats of clear butyrate and two or three coats of aluminum prior to the color coats. This kind of finish will burn, although the butyrate does tend to slow the burning rate.

We don't mean to infer that the Ceconite Process does not deserve its success, or that mechanics use it merely because they feel more comfortable working with familiar dopes. The Ceconite cloth beneath the conventional dopes has twice the life expectancy of Grade A cotton and therefore, as a practical matter, will undoubtedly last as long as it is possible to leave it on the airframe before the airframe itself needs refurbishing. Meanwhile, the butyrate dope finish can itself be rejuvenated at relatively low cost to stretch its service life.

The only problem that may develop, according to some mechanics, is that of over-tautness, which can result in airframe distortion on small airplanes as the butyrate finish ages, particularly if exposed to the sun a great deal in the Southwestern U.S. However, the people at Ceconite insist that this will not be a problem if their fabric is properly installed on the airframe—that is, 'Apply the sheet or slip cover the same degree of slack as you would with Grade A cotton or linen. That is, not baggy, not tight, just snug, but slightly on the loose side," and finish with "non-tautening" butyrate. (We'll go into step-by-step detail with each covering process in subsequent chapters.)

Perhaps the question of Dacron's service life, whether Ceconite or Poly-Fiber, should be considered against the background of several other considerations: 1) The average light aircraft has a total life expectancy of about 4,000 hours, a few as much as 6,000 hours total airframe time before being consigned to the boneyard. 2) Few people keep a given airplane more than five years. However, 3) the condition of the fabric and finish when you sell or trade makes a very big difference in what you get for that plane—and *that* determines, to a large extent, what it has cost to own and fly while you had it.

Since at least 75% of the cost of any re-cover job goes for labor, and since Grade A cotton now costs more than any of the synthetics, it seems safe to conclude that, if a given "rag-wing" is worth re-covering at all, one of the synthetics is the most sensible way to go.

We should mention that Dacron—just plain "Dacron," no brand name, no other description except weight—is offered by some aircraft supply houses as low as (at this writing) $1.95 per yard in 66-inch width, while 66-inch Ceconite has a list price of $4.75 per yard, and Poly-Fiber is $4.28. Razorback Fiberglas is $4.75 per yard in the 72-inch width. But the $1.95 no-name Dacron is no bargain, except perhaps for an airplane to be licensed in the Experimental category, because it will not be approved by the FAA under a Supplemental Type Certificate, which is necessary if it is to be applied to an ATC'd aircraft (that means a store-bought airplane, Jeb).

The Ceconite Dacrons, Stits Poly-Fiber, Eonnex, and Razorback Fiberglas cloth are approved by the FAA under Supplemental Type Certificates, and aircraft re-covered and finished with any of these processes are returned to service by way of the standard FAA Form 337, along with the appropriate entry in the airframe log. Each of these cloths will be identified as to brand name and type at 36-inch intervals along the selvage.

Ceconite's three weights are:

101 3.7 oz sq yd; average strength, approximately 130 lbs per inch width. Thread count 49 × 58.

102 2.8 oz sq yd; a fine weave having tensile properties slightly greater than Grade A cotton. Considered a standard replacement for cotton fabric when a smooth finish or weight saving is a consideration.

103 1.7 oz sq yd; a fine weave for use over plywood.

Razorback Fiberglas

The Razorback Method of covering aircraft dates back to the late fifties, as does the first use of the other synthetics now in general service. All had their problems, and all evolved, mostly through trial and error, into the practical systems that remain today; and of the several synthetics there's little doubt that Razorback's Fiberglas cloth is the least vulnerable to deterioration. Indeed, there's no evidence that it deteriorates at all; and when a test sample with 12 coats of dope was burned, all of the butyrate was consumed but the cloth remained intact with its original test strength.

In cold tests at 50-degrees F below zero, butyrate-finished Razorback bounced a 1-lb 5-oz cadmium ball free-falling from seven ft.

There is but one style of Razorback, weighing 3.92 oz sq yd, with a tensil strength of 160 lbs per inch in one direction, 150 lbs in the other. It is loosely woven and pre-treated with butyrate to aid prime coat adhesion. It is finished out with 12 coats of butyrate: five of prime and base (which *must* be sprayed; no brushes or rollers), two of clear non-tautening butyrate, three of non-tautening silver, and two color coats.

Since Razorback presumably will last forever, and since everyone knows that a butyrate finish will not, it's obvious that the

A HOG FOR PUNISHMENT

Aircraft covered with Razorback Fiberglas must display a Razorback decal on a vertical tail surface.

need for periodic dope rejuvenation can be expected with this combination.

Whether or not Razorback is more difficult to properly install than the Dacrons depends upon where you go for opinions. But this is true of nearly everything. Most of us tend to praise a system if we've learned to do it well, and knock the system at which we lack expertise. Nevertheless, it does appear that you have less control over the tautening process with Fiberglas cloth than with the Dacrons. That is, it doesn't have the degree of "shrinkability" that Dacron has; and the tautening that occurs results solely from the application of the buytrate base coats. The people at Razorback do not regard this as any big deal. They simply say that Razorback cloth "should not be installed under too much tension—just enough to remove the wrinkles and allow a snug fit." Along with Stits and Ceconite, Razorback places most emphasis on the finishing-out process.

Razorback recommends that the color coats be butyrate and that the polyurethanes and enamels not be used in combination with the base and silver coats of butyrate, the reason being, apparently, that incompatible solvent systems and differing expansion rates will result in peeling and cracking of the finish, and rejuvenation of the enamels is very difficult if not impossible.

Since Razorback Fiberglas cloth does not deteriorate, no pull or punch test is ever required by the FAA.

Razorback Aircraft Services President Sam Macre told this writer that "...most Razorback installation problems occur during the initial coat of dope and improper handling of the finishing tape during its installation."

Before working with Razorback cloth—or any other synthetic fabric covering system—a small test sample should be completed.

The Synthetics vs. Grade A Cotton

Although it seems apparent that the synthetics are superior to Grade A cotton on aircraft exteriors, we can't ignore cotton because airplanes are being covered with it every day. Why? Mostly because it finishes out so beautifully with expert handling.

During the preparation of this book the author flew to Enid, Oklahoma, where the new Great Lakes biplane is produced. We weren't sure whether personable Doug Champlin had selected Dacron or Fiberglas as a covering for the modern Great Lakes, but we felt that we should pin-down his finishing process because we had seen a new 'Lakes on a taxi strip a few months earlier when going into Wichita, and though we were some distance from it, its Gulfhawk color scheme, glistening in the sun like the coat of a wet seal, seemed glassy smooth. It was really beautiful.

We arrived at the Great Lakes facility—an impressive line of new, beige steel buildings on the east side of Enid Municipal—shortly after lunch and entered the building where final finishing is done. One side was lined with finished wings, standing in orderly rows, leading-edges down. On the other side was a number of fuselages, sans engines, awaiting their color coats. In the paint booth, a Great Lakes craftsman was inspecting an upper wing panel that had obviously been given its final color coat an hour or so earlier. Up close, we could see that this was indeed a nice finish, with no fabric weave visible.

"Hey, what are you covering these airplanes with?"

"Grade A cotton."

"I don't believe it!" We just weren't prepared for this. We had assumed that all new fabric-covered airplanes being built today would employ Dacron or Fiberglas.

"Uh, why cotton?"

"Because of the way it finishes out."

"You using nitrate underneath?"

"No. Butyrate all the way through."

"Sure looks nice," we said, and headed for the door. You can learn something every day.

On the way home we got to thinking and suddenly realized that we had been taking a lot for granted. Since Dacron and Fiberglas are far more durable than cotton, we had automatically concluded that all manufacturers of today's fabric-covered aircraft had "sensibly" switched to one of the synthetics. Better check. Let's see now, we've been to Alexandria, Minnesota and watched Bellanca build Vikings. They use Dacron. But what about Taylorcraft, Pitts, Maule, the Bellanca Champion Division and, yes, the latter-day Super Cubs?

Well, the modern T-Craft "Sportsman 100" is covered with Dacron and finished with butyrate, thank you.

The factory-built Pitts are covered with Dacron; the Maule fuselage with Fiberglas (wings are all-metal); and the Citabria, Scout, and Decathlon built by Bellanca's Champion Division are Dacron covered and finished with butyrate a la Ceconite. Our local Piper dealer says the Super Cub is still available on order, and is now covered with Dacron as far as he knows (We long ago gave up trying to get data from the Piper factory. Their public relations department apparently went underground in 1938).

So, all production aircraft that are fabric covered use the synthetics, except the Great Lakes.

We don't know what percentage of the 7,000 amateur-built airplanes in the U.S. employ syntetic covering; but we do know that

Bellance Vikings are Dacron covered. Wing is all-wood; plywood-covered under Dacron.

any Dacron covered aircraft in the used market will bring substantially more than the same machine wearing cotton.

The reason for this is that you can't really tell how long cotton fabric may last after it's a year or so old. The FAR's require that Grade A cotton test (minimum) 80 lbs new, and it must be replaced when it tests below 56 lbs tensile in both directions. The same specs apply to the synthetics. But cotton that tests in the 60 or 70 lbs range (or "high green") may last several years—or several months, mostly depending upon how it was finished out in the first place, and how it has been cared for since. You don't really know. You simply live from one annual inspection to the next.

On the other hand, Dacron two or three years old will invariably still test above 100 lbs if properly finished when installed. Fiberglas, as mentioned earlier, need never be tested for strength since it does not deteriorate.

For comparison purposes, Stits Aircraft says, "Our exposure tests have verified that Dacron cloth will deteriorate in direct proportion to exposure to the ultraviolet rays from the sun. Bare Dacron test panels deteriorate in eight months from exposure to the sun in Southern California. Bare cotton and linen deteriorate in three to four months. Applying this same ratio, it is reasonable to expect Dacron covering to last at least twice as long as cotton or linen covering under identical exposure conditions..."

Since Grade A cotton fabric now costs about 20% more than Dacron or Razorback cloth, the case for cotton would seem to rest solely on the outstanding finish it's possible to achieve with it.

Automotive & Industrial Finishes

The fact that bare cotton will last but 90 days, and bare Dacron but eight months exposed to the elements measures the true value of a proper finish on exterior aircraft fabrics. Just about everything has been tried, and we return to Stits Aircraft for some thoughts on automotive and industrial products that are often used:

"Synthetic enamel is the most common automotive finish used on aircraft fabric. It is more weather resistant than pigmented nitrate or butyrate dope finishes and dries to a good gloss, but it will become brittle in a shorter length of time in sunlight due to oxidation of the vegetable oils.

"Synthetic enamel was developed in the thirties to replace lacquer as an automotive metal finish and was not intended to be used on flexible fabric surfaces. It is an alkyd resin and is not

Almost invisible finishing tapes and dentless leading edges are two signs of good craftsmanship in the re-cover job on this Stearman.

compatible with the solvents used in nitrate and butyrate dopes, lacquer, or the Stits Poly-Dope. When synthetic enamel is over-coated with any of these materials, the solvents penetrate and swell or "lift" the enamel. To make suitable fabric repairs, the synthetic enamel coat is removed. There are many manufacturers of synthetic (alkyd) enamel, each with its own particular formula depending upon the proposed end use. However, the basic characteristics of synthetic enamel are the same whether it is labeled automotive, industrial, or aircraft enamel.

"An often used 'quickie' method of two or three coats of nitrate dope on Dacron, three coats of aluminum pigmented butyrate dope, then five or six heavy coats of automotive metal primer, each sanded to completely hide the fabric weave and tapes, and a finish of automotive synthetic enamel, looks beautiful for about a year, and then the primer and enamel starts to peel from the aluminum pigmented butyrate dope. Incompatible thermo expansion and incompatible solvent systems coupled with oxidation and decreasing flexibility of the enamel are the causes.

"Cross linking (two-part) polyurethane enamels which have been formulated for the most durable finish on metal surfaces are by necessity very hard, and by characteristics very smooth and glossy and will look outstanding on fabric surfaces, however, will eventually crack because they will not take the continued flexing imposed on fabric surfaces. Urethane enamel finishes cannot be rejuvenated and complete stripping is the only practical procedure to elimnate any cracking problem..."

The Eonnex Process

Eonair, Inc., was formed by electronics engineer William G. Lott in 1957 to market a synthetic fabric, "Eonite," that Lott had developed, primarily for agricultural aircraft. This fabric was a special formula that has the appearance and feel of Nylon, and was laminated to a fine layer of Fiberglas. It appears to have been an excellent fabric, but the laminating had to be done with thermosetting resins in a process that demanded special training of the mechanics, and this severely limited the use of Eonite.

In mid-1960, Eonair placed on the market its Eonnex covering process which abandoned the Fiberglas lamination. The uncoated Eonnex 205 cloth weighed 4 oz sq/yd and had a tensile strength of 150 lbs. It was resin-treated in manufacture to solve the finish-adhesion problems other synthetics had experienced and, indeed, required but three finish coats altogether. This resulted in substantial savings of labor, cost, and weight.

Then, in 1976, when Eonair announced development of its new emulsion type coatings and adhesives, Bill Lott could claim that he had reduced the aircraft covering procedure to its simplest, least expensive form—with a cover possessing a life expectancy of eighteen years or more.

The use of the new emulsions markedly reduce the skill formerly needed to apply the coatings and surface tapes properly. These coatings have greatly improved flexibility and fire resistance, as well as easier application (they may be applied with a pad), faster dry, and extremely low toxicity. Except for the final glaze coat, they are thinned and cleaned with water. The emulsion coatings contain no flammable solvents, and can be applied under most weather conditions without blushing.

The continuous coating that is factory-applied to Eonnex takes the place of a primer and some of the filler coating, thus reducing cost and the number of coating applications required after installation.

Eonnex fabric is heat-tautened (with a low-cost electric iron especially designed for this work and marketed by Eonair), and requires but one sanding. The non-tautening Eonnex coatings will not shrink with age, require a minimum of shop ventilation to use, and no rejuvenation is ever required.

The new Eonnex 7605 cloth is essentially the same as the earlier 205, with the same weight and strength characteristics; and Eonair's Bill Lott says, "While we advertise that other coverings cost over 40% more than our 7600 Series, in practice the comparisons I have made indicates that they are over 50% more in materials cost alone, there are, of course, great labor savings."

As mentioned above, Eonnex 7605 fabric is factory pre-coated, eliminating the previously required primer and first filler coating. The fabric is heat-shrunk on the airframe without damage to, or softening of the pre-coat. The pre-coat has a built-in indicator that temporarily changes color when the fabric has been heated to shrinking temperature.

Eonnex 7606 fabric is similar to 7605 except that it is lighter in weight and possesses a finer weave. Its tensile strength is 115 lbs.

Eonnex Cement and Activators, 7602 and 7603, constitute a high tenacity adhesive system. It is used for the rapid structural attachment of the fabric, and for the installation of surface tapes and other reinforcement.

The Eonnex Surface Tapes #7604 are pre-coated. This permits the use of a minimum of filler for a smooth finish. They are installed directly over the pre-coated fabric.

Eonnex Surface Tapes #7624 are an alternative to the pre-coated tapes. They are made from 7606 fabric and may be heat-shrunk to conform to compound curves.

Eonnex 7601 Filler Coating is a very high solids material. Only one coat is required prior to finish painting. No solvent is needed, and clean up is with water. This coating may be applied with spray gun or applicator pad. It will not burn, wet or dry. Under good drying conditions, the coating will be ready to sand and paint in less than 15 minutes. It will not blush.

Eonnex covering is color coated after the filler (7601) coating has been applied. Pigmented dope may be used, but for best results Eonnex 7640 color, over-coated with 7630 Clear Urethane Enamel Glaze, is recommended. This combination has the flexibility necessary to match the substrate and provide crack resistance. It is a high-gloss, durable finishing system, available in more than 1,000 colors for both fabric and metal. This permits a close match of virtually any color in use.

Eonnex 7600 Series materials may be used to repair or complete unfinished coverings made from the older type Eonnex materials.

The FAA-approved Master Eligibility List for the Eonnex Process includes most aircraft that have any fabric covered components. A prototype inspection is not required for listed aircraft. Eonnex products are, of course, manufactured under FAA-PMA, and the approval basis is Supplemental Type Certificate SA4-1210 and SG4-1240. In other words, Eonnex, along with the other synthetics herein described, is thoroughly tested, approved, and legal.

Detailed instructions for the application of Eonnex materials are contained in Chapter 8.

Chapter 2
FAA Advisories AC
43.13-1A & 2, and AC 65-15

The instructions accompanying any synthetic fabric covering process for aircraft all reference FAA Advisory AC 43.13-1A & 2, which sets forth the standards that must be met whatever the fabric type. Implementation of those standards are expanded upon in AC 65-15. In later chapters, we'll discuss individually the several synthetic fabric processes; but first, the general data from these FAA Advisory Circulars will provide a sound and useful (and legal) basis for whatever process you employ:

In the original manufacture of a fabric covered aircraft, the quality and strength of the fabric, surface tape, lacing cord, thread, etc., are determined by the aircraft's never-exceed speed and the pounds per square foot of wing loading. The never-exceed speed for a particular aircraft is that safe speed beyond which it should never be operated. The aircraft wing loading is determined by dividing its total wing planform area (in square feet) into the maximum allowable gross weight.

All fabric, surface tape, reinforcing tape, machine thread, lacing cord, etc., used for re-covering or repairing an aircraft's cover should be of high grade aircraft textile material. The materials must also be at least as good a quality and of equivalent strength as those originally used by the aircraft manufacturer.

The following definitions are presented to simplify the discussion of aircraft fabrics.

1. **Warp**—The direction along the length of the fabric.
2. **Warp ends**—The woven threads that run the length of the fabric.

3. **Filling, woof,** or **weft**—The direction across the width of the fabric.
4. **Count**—The number of threads per inch in warp or filling.
5. **Bias**—A cut, fold, or seam made diagonally in the warp or fill threads.
6. **Calendering**—The process of ironing fabric by thread-it wet between a series of hot and cold rollers to produce a smooth finish.
7. **Mercerization**—The process of dipping cotton yarn or fabric in a hot solution of diluted caustic soda. This treatment causes the material to shrink and acquire greater strength and luster.
8. **Sizing**—Material, such as starch, used to stiffen the yarns for ease in weaving the cloth.
9. **Pinked edge**—An edge which has been cut by machine or shears in a continuous series of V's to prevent raveling.
10. **Selvage edge**—An edge of cloth, tape, or webbing woven to prevent raveling.

Cotton Fabrics

Grade A airplane cloth is a four-ounce mercerized fabric made of high-grade long staple cotton. It is calendered to reduce the thickness and lay the nap so that the surface will be smooth. There are from 80 to 84 threads per inch, warp and fill. The minimum tensile strength is 80 pounds per inch of width, warp and fill. The term "four-ounce" indicates that the normal weight of the finished cloth is four ounces per square yard for 36 and 42-inch widths. Fabric of this grade and weight is acceptable for covering any aircraft fabric surface.

Linen Fabrics

Unbleached linen fabric is used extensively in England and to a limited degree in the U.S. This fabric is practically identical to Grade A cotton fabric insofar as weight, strength, and threads per inch are concerned. (Editor's note: This is the exact wording in AC-65-15. But it is our experience that Irish linen will normally outlast Grade A cotton by 25 percent.)

Dacron Fabrics

Dacron is a very smooth, monofilament polyester fiber manufactured by the condensation of dimethyl terephthalate and ethylene glycol. A generally standard style and weight of Dacron cloth has evolved for use as aircraft covering. It is a plain weave with a weight of about 3.7 ounces per square yard. This heavy duty fabric

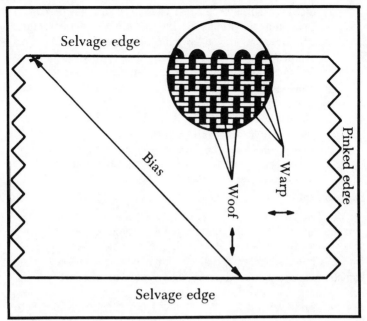

Fabric terms.

has a tensile strength of approximately 148 pounds per square inch, and can be used to replace Grade A cotton and linen fabrics.

A fine weave, medium weight Dacron fabric is used when a minimum covering weight and very smooth finish are desired. The medium weight fabric has a tensile strength of approximately 96 pounds per square inch, weighs about 2.7 ounces per square yard, and can also be used as a replacement for Grade A cotton fabric.

Glass Cloth

Glass cloth, or Fiberglas cloth, is made from fine-spun glass filaments which are woven into a strong, tough fabric. Glass cloth used for aircraft covering has a plain weave and weighs about 4.5 ounces per square yard (Razorback says 3.92 ounces per square yard—author). It is not affected by moisture, mildew, chemicals, or acids. It is also fire resistant.

Glass cloth applications generally fall into the following classes:

1. Class A is a complete or partial reinforcement of a serviceable fabric covering. No direct structural attachment of the glass cloth is provided. This composite covering is considered airworthy until the underlying conventional fabric deteriorates below 70% of its original strength or 56 pounds tensil test.

2. Class B is a reinforcement of a fabric covering wherein the glass cloth is provided with the same direct structural attachment as that used with the original covering. This composite covering is considered airworthy until the underlying conventional fabric has deteriorated to a strength-less than 50% of the minimum tensile strength values when new.
3. Class C is replacement coverings applied either independently or over a conventional covering. The glass covering should possess all the necessary characteristics for airworthiness and is in no way dependent upon the underlying covering if one is present.

Surface Tape

Surface tape is the finishing tape that is doped over each rib or seam to cover the stitching and provides a neat, smooth, finished appearance. It can be obtained with serrated or pinked edges, or with a straightedge impregnated with a sealing compound. The compound-impregnated edges or pinked edges provide better adhesion to the fabric covering.

Surface tape is made from Grade A fabric in widths from 1-¼ to 3-¾ inches, and from glider fabric in 1-½ and 2-inch widths. Cotton surface tape may be used with Grade A cotton, linen, or Dacron fabric. Surface tape is also available in Dacron fabric, which should be the first choice when covering an aircraft with Dacron. Linen surface tape frequently is used with fiber glass covering, especially for covering screw-heads. If fiber glass tape is used, it is difficult to remove the irregularities caused by the screw-heads. Using linen tape to cover screw-heads gives a smooth, finished appearance.

Surface tape or finishing tape should be placed over all lacing, seams (both machine and hand-sewn), corners, edges, and places where wear is likely to occur. Two-inch tape generally is used for this purpose. Pinked surface tape is sometimes applied over the trailing edges of control surface and airfoils. For such application the tape should be at least three inches wide and should be notched along both edges at intervals not exceeding six inches. If the tape begins to separate from the trailing edge, it will tear at a notched section and thereby prevent loosening of the entire strip.

Tape is applied over a second wet coat of dope which is applied after the first coat has dried. Another coat of dope is applied immediately over the tape. The tape adheres firmly to the covering because both surfaces of the tape are impregnated with dope.

Reinforcing Tape

Reinforcing tape is used over ribs between the fabric covering and the rib stitching to prevent the stitching cord from cutting through the fabric. It is also used for cross-bracing ribs and for binding. Reinforcing tape is fabricated from cotton, Dacron, fiber glass (everyone spells this differently. "Fiberglas" is a registered trade name—author), or linen materials. A tape made from fiber glass on acetate with a pressure-sensitive adhesive is also available.

Reinforcing tape is available in a variety of widths conforming to the different widths of ribs or rib capstrips. The tape should be slightly wider than the member it covers. A double width is sometimes necessary for very wide members.

Reinforcing tape is used under all lacing to protect the fabric from cuts. This tape should be under a slight tension and secured at both ends. For wings with plywood or metal leading edge covering, the reinforcing tape is extended only to the front spar on the upper and lower surfaces.

Sewing Thread

Thread is made by a right or left twist that is identified by various terms. Machine, machine twist, left twist, or Z-twist indicates a left-twist thread. S-twist indicates a right-twist thread.

An unbleached silk-finish, left-twist cotton thread is used to machine sew cotton fabrics. Silk-finish refers to a thread which has been sized to produce a hard, glazed surface. This finish prevents the thread from fraying and becoming weak. A thread having a tensile strength of at least five pounds per single strand should be used. An unbleached white cotton, silk-finish thread is used in hand sewing cotton fabrics. This thread must have a strength of at least 14 pounds per single strand.

Dacron fabrics are sewn with Dacron sewing thread. Glass fabrics, when sewn, are sewn with special synthetic threads.

Thread for hand sewing and lacing cord should be waxed lightly before using. The wax should not exceed 20% of the weight of the finished cord. A beeswax free from paraffin should be used for this pupose.

Rib Lacing Cord

Rib lacing cord is used to sew the fabric to the ribs. The cord must be strong to transmit the suction on the upper surface of the wing from the fabric to the ribs, which in turn carry the load into the main wing structure. The cord must also resist fraying caused by the flexing action of the fabric and wing ribs. Dacron, linen, glass, or cotton cords are used for rib lacing.

Special Fasteners

When repairs are made to fabric surfaces attached by special mechanical methods, the original types of fastening should be duplicated. Screws and washers are used on several models of aircraft, and wire clips are used on others. Screws or clips may not be used unless they were used by the manufacturer of the aircraft. When self-tapping screws are used to attach fabric to metal rib structure, the following procedure should be observed: Worn or distorted holes should be re-drilled, and a screw one size larger than the original used as a replacement. The length of the screw should be sufficient so that at least two threads of the grip (threaded part) extend through and beyond the rib capstrip. A thin washer, preferably celluloid, should be used under the heads of screws, and pinked-edge tape should be doped over each screw-head.

Seams

A seam consists of a series of stitches joining two or more pieces of material. Properly formed seam stitches possess the following characteristics:

1. Strength. A seam must have sufficient strength to withstand the strain to which it will be subjected. The strength of a seam is affected by the type of stitch and thread used, number of stitches per inch of seam, tightness of the seam, and the size and type of needle used.
2. Elasticity. The elasticity of the material to be sewed determines the degree of elasticity desirable in the seam. Elasticity is affected by the quality of thread used, tension of the thread, length of stitch, and type of seam.
3. Durability. The durability of a seam is determined by the durability of the material. Tightly woven fabrics are more durable than loosely woven fabrics which tend to work or slide upon each other. For this reason the stitches must be tight and the thread well set into the material to minimize abrasion and wear caused by contact with external objects.
4. Good appearance. The appearance of a seam is largely controlled by its construction. However, appearance should not be the principal factor when constructing covers.

Sewed Seams

Machine-sewed seams should be of the folded-fell or French-fell types. A plain lapped seam is satisfactory where selvage edges or pinked edges are joined.

All machine sewing should have two rows of stitches with eight to ten stitches per inch. A lockstitch is preferred. All seams should be as smooth as possible and provide adequate strength. Stitches

Ceconite wing ready for final color coats.

should be approximately 1/16th inch from the edge of the seam, and from ¼ to ⅜ inch from the adjacent row of stitches.

Hand sewing is necessary to close the final openings in the covering. Final openings in wooden wing coverings are sometimes closed by tacking, but sewing is preferable. A ½-inch hem should be turned under on all seams to be hand sewn. Preparatory to hand sewing, the fabric on wooden wings can be held under tension by tacks; fabric on metal wings can be pinned to adhesive tape pasted to the trailing edge of the wings.

Hand sewing or tacking should begin where machine sewing stops and should continue to the point where machine sewing or uncut fabric is again reached. Hand sewing should be locked at six-inch intervals and the seams should be properly finished with a lockstitch and a knot (see accompanying drawing). Where hand sewing or permanent tacking is necessary, the fabric should be so cut that it can be doubled under before it is sewed or permanently tacked. After hand sewing has been completed, the temporary tacks should be removed. In hand sewing there should be a minimum of four stitches per inch.

A double-stitched lap joint should be covered with pinked-edge surface tape at least four inches wide.

Spanwise seams on the upper or lower surface should be sewed with a minimum of protuberance. The seam should be covered with pinked-edge tape at least three inches wide.

A spanwise seam sewed at the trailing edge should be covered with pinked-edge surface tape at least three inches wide. V-shaped notches at least one-inch deep and one-inch wide should be cut in both edges of the surface tape used to cover spanwise seams on trailing edges, especially the trailing edges of control surfaces. The notches should be so spaced as not to exceed six-inch intervals. On tape less than three inches wide, the notches should be one-third the tape width. If the tape begins to separate because of poor adhesion or other causes, it will tear at a notched section, thus preventing progressive loosening of the entire length of tape.

Sewed seams parallel to the line of flight (chordwise) may be placed over a rib, but the seams should be placed so that the lacing will not be through them.

Doped Seams

For a lapped and doped spanwise seam on a metal or wood-covered leading edge, lap the fabric at least four inches and cover with pinked-edge surface tape at least four inches wide.

For a lapped and doped spanwise seam at the trailing edge, lap the fabric at least four inches and cover with pinked-edge surface tape at least three inches wide.

Structure Inspection and Preparation

The inspection and preparation of the aircraft structure prior to covering are discussed in detail in a following chapter.

Covering Practices, General

The method of fabric attachment should be identical, as far as strength and reliability are concerned, to the method used by the airplane's manufacturer. Fabric may be applied so that either the warp or fill threads are parallel to the line of flight. Either the envelope method or blanket method of covering is acceptable.

The envelope method consists of sewing together widths of fabric cut to specified dimensions and machine sewed to form an envelope that can be drawn over the frame. The trailing and outer edges of the covering should be machine sewn unless the component is not favorably shaped for sewing, in which case the fabric should be joined by hand sewing.

In the blanket method of covering, widths of fabrics of sufficient lengths are sewn together to form a blanket over the surfaces of the frame. The trailing and outer edges of the covering should be joined by a plain overthrow or baseball stitch. For airplanes with a placarded never-exceed speed of 150 mph or less, the blanket may be lapped at least one inch and doped to the frame or the blanket; it may be lapped at least four inches at the nose of metal or wood-covered leading edges, doped, and finished with pinked-edge surface tape at least eight inches wide. In both the envelope and blanket coverings, the fabric should be cut in lengths sufficient to pass completely around the frame, starting at the trailing edge and returning to the trailing edge. Seams parallel to the line of flight are preferable, but spanwise seams are acceptable.

Before applying cotton or linen fabrics, brush on several coats of clear, full-bodied nitrate dope on all points to which the fabric edges will be cemented. If the structure is not doped, the dope used to cement the fabric edges will be absorbed by the surface as well as by the fabric. This will result in a poor bond to the structure after the dope has dried. Dacron fabric can be attached to the structure by using either nitrate dope or specially formulated cements.

After securing the cover, cotton and linen fabrics may be water-shrunk to remove wrinkles and excess slack. The fabric must be dried thoroughly before doping begins. Dacron may be heat-shrunk by using an electric iron set at 425 degrees F, or by using a reflector heater. Do not apply excessive heat, because the Dacron, as well as the understructures of the wood, may be damaged.

Dacron shrinking should be done in several stages on opposite sides to shrink the entire area uniformly. Remove the excess slack with the initial application of heat. The second pass will then shrink the fabric to the desired tautness and remove most of the remaining wrinkles. Non shrinking nitrate and butyrate dopes are available and produce no further shrinking or tightening. Regular dopes will pull the fibers and strands together and can damage light structures. A nonshrinking dope must be used when Dacron is heat-shrunk to its final tautness.

Taping

Sewed seams, lapped edges, and rib stitching or screws must be covered with pinked-edge surface tape. Use surface tape having the same properties as the fabric used for covering.

Apply the tape by first laying down a wet coat of dope, followed immediately by the tape. Press the tape into the dope. Work out any trapped air and apply a coat of dope over the surface of the tape.

Re-Covering With Glass Cloth

Fiber glass fabrics are acceptable for re-covering or reinforcing an aircraft surface, provided the material meets the requirements of Military Specifications MIL-C-9084, MIL-Y-1140, and MIL-G-1140. The tensile strength of the glass cloth should be at least equivalent to the tensile strength of the fabric originally installed on the aircraft. The chemical finish of the glass cloth should be chemically compatible with the dope or resin to be used.

Either the blanket or envelope method of reinforcement should be used on treated fabrics that can be sewn. Untreated fabric that cannot be sewn may be applied in overlapping sections. The practices recommended for doped seams should be used. Where the glass cloth is applied only to the upper surface of the wings for hail protection, it should wrap around the trailing edge at least one inch and extend from the trailing edge up to and around the leading edge and back approximately to the front spar. Before starting the work, make certain that the bonding agents used will be satisfactory. Blistering or poor adhesion can occur when using bonding agents which are not chemically compatible with the present finish on the aircraft, or which have already deteriorated with age. A simple means of determining this is to apply a small piece of the reinforced cloth to the original cover, using the proposed finishing process. The test sample should be visually checked the next day for blistering or poor adhesion.

When butyrate dope is used to bond glass cloth, the finishing may be accomplished in the following manner:

1. Thoroughly clean the surface and allow to dry. If the surface has been waxed or previously covered with other

protective coatings, thoroughly remove at least the top finish coat. After placing the glass cloth on the surface, brush out smoothly and thoroughly with butyrate dope thinner and 10% (by volume) retarder.

2. Apply a heavy coat of butyrate dope between all glass cloth overlaps. When dry, brush in butyrate rejuvenator and allow to set until the surface has again drawn tight.

3. Install reinforcing tape and structural attachments (Class B) and dope on finishing tape (cotton is recommended); then brush in one coat of 50% thinner and 50% butyrate dope.

4. Follow by conventional finishing schedules, which call for application of one or more coats of full-bodied clear butyrate dope, two spray coats of aluminum pigmented butyrate dope, light surface sanding, and two spray coats of pigmented butyrate dope.

When resin is used to bond the glass cloth, after surface cleaning, the finishing may be done in the following manner:

1. Rejuvenate the doped surface. After placing the glass cloth on the surface, brush in thoroughly a coat of resin. Saturate overlapped areas thoroughly and allow to cure.

2. Brush in a second coat of resin smoothly and evenly and allow to cure. The finished surface should not be considered completed until all the holes between the weave of the cloth are filled flush with resin.

3. After water sanding, paint the surface with one coat of primer surfacer and finish as desired.

Install drain grommets and inspection holes as provided in the original cover.

When using glass fabric to reinforce movable control surfaces, check to ascertain that no change has been made in their static and dynamic balance.

Covering Wings

Wings may be covered with fabric by the envelope, blanket, or combination method. The envelope method is preferable and should be used whenever possible.

The envelope method of covering wings consists of sewing together several widths of fabric of definite dimensions and then running a transverse (spanwise) seam to make an envelope or sleeve. The advantage of the envelope method is that practically all sewing is by machine, and there is an enormous saving of labor in fitting the covering. The sleeve is pulled over the wing through its one open end, which is hand-sewed or tacked. If the envelope is of the proper dimensions, it will fit the wing snugly. When possible, the spanwise seam should be placed along the trailing edge.

In the blanket method several widths of fabric are machine-sewed together and placed over the wing with a hand-sewed, spanwise seam along the trailing edge. Care must be taken to apply tension over the whole surface.

The combination uses the envelope method as much as possible, and the blanket method on the remainder of the covering. This method is applicable to wings with obstructions or recesses that prevent full application of an envelope.

After the cover is sewn in place and shrunk, reinforcing tape of at least the width of the capstrips is placed over each rib and the fabric is laced to each rib. Except on very thick wings the lacing passes completely around the rib. On thick wings the lacing passes around one chord member only, but both top and bottom surfaces must be laced in this manner. Lacing should be as near as possible to the capstrip. The rib should not have any rough or sharp edges in contact with the lacing, or it will fray and break. Each time the lacing cord goes around the rib it is tied, and then the next stitch is made at the specified distance.

In order not to overstress the lacing, it is necessary to space the stitches a definite distance apart, depending upon the speed of the airplane. Because of the additional buffeting caused by the propeller slipstream, the stitching must be spaced closer on all ribs included within the slipstream. It is customary to use this closer spacing on the ribs just outboard of the propeller diameter as well.

The stitch spacing should not exceed the approved spacing on the original covering of the aircraft. If the spacing cannot be ascertained because of destruction of the covering, acceptable rib-stitch spacing may be determined from the accompanying chart. The lacing holes should be placed as closely as possible to the capstrip to minimize the tendency of the cord to tear the fabric. All lacing cord should be lightly waxed with beeswax for protection.

Anti-Tear Strips

In very high speed airplanes difficulty is often experienced with the rib lacing breaking or with fabric tearing in the slipstream.

On aircraft with never-exceed speeds in excess of 250 mph anti-tear strips are recommended under reinforcing tape on the upper surface of the wings and on the bottom surface of that part of the wing in the slipstream. Where the anti-tear strip is used on both the top and bottom surfaces, extend it continuously up to and around the leading edge and back to the trailing edge. Where the strip is used only on the top surface, carry it up to and around the leading edge and

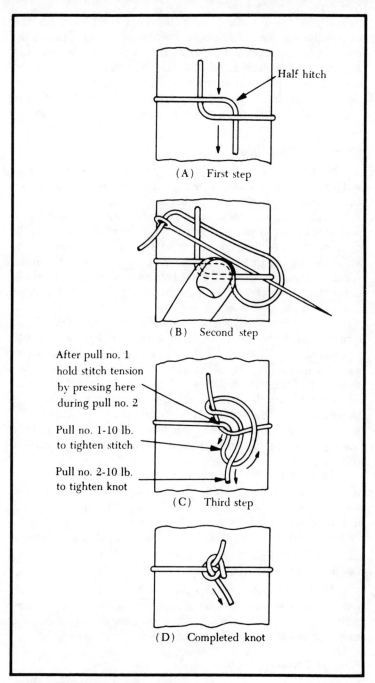

(A) First step

Half hitch

(B) Second step

After pull no. 1
hold stitch tension
by pressing here
during pull no. 2

Pull no. 1-10 lb.
to tighten stitch

Pull no. 2-10 lb.
to tighten knot

(C) Third step

(D) Completed knot

Standard knot for rib lacing.

back on the lower surface as far aft as the front spar. For this purpose the slipstream should be considered as being equal to the propeller diameter, plus one extra rib space on each side. Cut anti-tear strips from the same material as that used for covering, and cut them wide enough to extend beyond the reinforcing tape on each side to engage the lacing cord. Attach the strips by applying dope to that part of the fabric to be covered by the strip and applying dope freely over the strip.

Single-Loop Wing Lacing

Both surfaces of the fabric covering on wings and control surfaces should be securely fastened to the ribs by lacing cord or any other method originally used by the manufacturer.

All sharp edges against which the lacing cord may bear must be protected by tape to prevent abrasion of the cord. Separate lengths of lacing cord should be joined by the space knot shown in the accompanying illustration. The common square knot, which has a very low slippage resistance, should not be used to splice lengths of lacing cord. The utmost care should be used to assure uniform tension and security of all stitches.

Rib stitching usually is started at the leading edge of the rib and continued to the trailing edge. If the leading edge is covered with plywood or metal, start the lacing immediately aft of these coverings. The first or starting stitch is made with a double loop, using the method illustrated in the accompanying drawing. All subsequent stitches can be made with a single loop. The spacing between the starting stitch and the next stitch should be one-half the normal stitch spacing. Where stitching ends, such as at the rear spar and the trailing edge, the last two stitches should be spaced at one-half normal spacing.

All stitches, other than the starting stitch, must be tied off using the standard knot for rib lacing. Tie-off knots usually are placed on the lower surface of low-wing aircraft and on the upper surface of high-wing aircraft to improve the final appearances of the surfaces. Under no circumstances should tie-off knots be pulled back through the lacing holes.

Double-Loop Wing Lacing

The double-loop lacing illustrated in the accompanying drawing represents a method for obtaining higher strengths than are possible with the standard single lacing. When using the double-loop lacing, make the tie-off knot as illustrated.

Fuselage Covering

Fuselages are covered by either the sleeve or blanket method, similar to the methods described for covering wings. In the sleeve or envelope method several widths of fabric are joined by machine-sewed seams to form a sleeve that will fit snugly when drawn over the end of the fuselage. When the sleeve is in place, all seams should be as nearly parallel as possible to the longitudinal members of the fuselage.

In the blanket method all seams are machine-sewed, except one final longitudinal seam along the bottom center of the fuselage. In some cases the blanket is put on in two or three sections and hand-sewed on the fuselage. All seams should run fore and aft.

Fuselage Lacing

Fabric lacing is also necessary on deep fuselages and on those where former strips and ribs shape the fabric to a curvature. In the latter case the fabric should be laced to the formers at intervals. The method of attaching the fabric to the fuselage should be at least the equivalent in strength and reliability to that used by the manufacturer of the airplane.

Ventilation, Drain, & Inspection Openings

The interior of covered sections is ventilated and drained to prevent moisture from accumulating and damaging the structure. Ventilation and drainage holes are provided and the edges reinforced with plastic, aluminum, or brass grommets.

Grommets are doped to the underside of fabric with the second coat of dope. Install drain grommets on the underside of airfoils, at the center of the underside in each fuselage bay, located so that the best possible drainage is effected. On seaplanes, installation of special shielded or marine grommets is recommended to prevent the entry of spray. Also, use this type of grommet on landplanes in that part of the structure which is subject to splash from the landing gear when operating from wet and muddy fields. Dope plastic-type

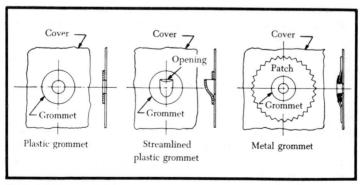

Typical drain grommets.

grommets directly to the covering. When brass grommets are used, mount them on fabric patches and then dope them to the covering. After the dope scheme is completed, open the drainholes by cutting out the fabric with a small-bladed knife. Do not open drain grommets by punching.

Storage Conditions

It is generally assumed that a hangared aircraft is protected from fabric deterioration. However, premature deterioration can occur, especially on aircraft stored in an unheated hangar that has a dirt floor. During the day, sun shining on the roof raises the air temperature in the hangar. This warm air absorbs moisture from the ground. When the air cools, the absorbed moisture condenses and settles on the aircraft. Atmospheric pressure changes draw the damp air into the airframe enclosures. These conditions provide an ideal situation for promoting mildew growth.

When storing fabric-covered aircraft, all openings large enough for rodents to enter should be taped. Uric acid from mice can rot fabric. It can also corrode metal parts such as ribs, spars, and fittings. Mice will also dine on rib lacing, while hornets or mud daubers that take up residence inside a wing or fuselage can furnish some airborne thrills that you'd just as soon do without.

Checking Condition of Doped Fabric

The condition of doped fabric should be checked at intervals sufficient to determine that the strength of the fabric has not deteriorated to the point where airworthiness of the aircraft is affected.

The areas selected for test should be those known to deteriorate most rapidly. The top surfaces generally deteriorate more rapidly than the side or bottom surfaces. When contrasting colors are used on an aircraft, the fabric will deteriorate more rapidly under the darker colors. The dark colors absorb more heat than the lighter colors. The warmer inner surface of the fabric under the darker color absorbs more moisture from the air inside the wing or fuselage. When the surface cools, this moisture condenses and the fabric under the dark area becomes moist and promotes mildew growth in a localized area. When checking cloth fabric that has been reinforced by applying fiber glass, peel back the glass cloth in the areas to be tested. Test the underlying cloth in the conventional manner.

Checking fabric surfaces is made easier by using a fabric punch tester. There are several acceptable fabric punch testers on the market; one such tester incorporates a penetrating cone as illustrated. Fabric punch testers are designed for use on the dope-finished-fabric surface of the aircraft and give only a general indication of the degree of deterioration in the strength of the fabric covering. Thier advantage is that they may be used easily and quickly to test the fabric without cutting samples for laboratory test. If a fabric punch tester indicates that the fabric strength is marginal, a laboratory test should be performed.

When using a punch tester similar to the one illustrated, place the tip on the doped fabric. With the tester held perpendicular to the surface, apply pressure with a slight rotary action until the flange of the tester contacts the fabric. The condition of the fabric is indicated by a color-banded plunger that projects from the top of the tester. The last exposed band is compared to a chart furnished by the manufacturer of the tester to determine fabric condition.

The test should be repeated at various positions on the fabric. The lowest reading obtained, other than an isolated repairable area, should be considered representative of the fabric condition as a whole. Fabrics that test just within the acceptable range should be checked frequently thereafter to ensure continued serviceability.

The punch tester makes only a small hole (approximately ½-inch in diameter) or a depression in the fabric that can be repaired quickly by doping on a two or three-inch patch.

Tensile Testing of Fabric

Tensile testing of fabric is a practical means of determining whether a fabric covering has deteriorated to the point where recovering is necessary. A typical fabric tensil tester is illustrated.

Fabric specimens must be tensile tested in the undoped condition. Use acetone dope thinner or other appropriate thinning agents to remove the finishing materials from the test specimen.

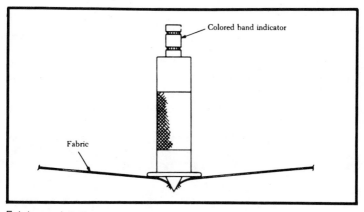

Colored band indicator

Fabric

Fabric punch tester.

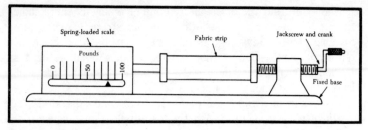

Fabric tensile tester.

A sample of the fabric to be tested is cut to exactly 1-½ inches in width and to a sufficient length (usually six inches) to allow insertion in the fabric tester. Usually, each edge of the strip is frayed ¼-inch, reducing the woven width to one inch. The ends of the fabric strip are fastened securely in the clamps of the tester. As the crank of the tester is turned, the threaded jackscrew is backed out, thus gradually increasing the tension (pull) on the fabric against the resistance of the spring-loaded scale until the fabric strip breaks. The scale reading, taken at the moment the fabric strip breaks, indicates the strength of the fabric in pounds per inch.

Chapter 3
Dopes and Doping, General

To tighten fabric covering and to make it airtight and watertight, brush or spray the cloth with dope. A tight fabric cover is essential to securing and holding the cross-sectional shape of the airfoil to the form given by the ribs. This dope also protects the fabric from deterioration by weather or sunlight and, when polished, imparts a smooth surface to the fabric and reduces skin friction in flight. Dopes must be applied under ideal conditions to obtain satisfactory and consistent results. A clean, fresh, dry atmosphere with a temperature above 70 degrees F and a relative humidity below 60%, combined with good ventilation, is necessary in the dope room. The dope must be of the proper consistency and be applied uniformly over the entire surface.

Dopes will deteriorate seiously if stored in too warm a place for a long period. The temperature should not exceed 60 degrees F for long-time storage and must not exeed 80 degrees F for periods up to four months. Precautions against fire should be taken whenever dope is stored or used because of its flammable nature. Dope and paint rooms that are not located in a separate building should be isolated from the rest of the building by metal partitions and fireproof doors.

As stated previously, the most desirable condition in a dope room is a temperature above 70 degrees F and a relatively humidity below 60%. At lower temperatures the dope will not flow freely without the addition of excessive thinners. The relative humidity can be lowered by raising the temperature if the dope shop is not equipped with humidity control. To condition fabric surfaces to the desired temperature and moisture conditions, allow them to stand about four hours in the dope room after covering and prior to doping.

The number of coats of dope applied to a fabric surface depends on the finish desired. It is customary to apply two to four coats of clear dope followed by two coats of aluminum pigmented dope. Sufficient clear dope should be applied to increase the weight of the fabric by 2-¼ to 2-½ ounces per square yard. The clear dope film should weigh this amount after drying for 72 hours. With fabric weighing four ounces, the total weight of fabric and dope is approximately 9-½ ounces per square yard.

You will understand that we're talking here about the minimum dope coverage, applied to Grade A cotton cloth, as per FAA recommendation in AC-65-15 and AC 43.13-1A & 2. These are the basic references and standards for all cloth covering methods, except for specific departures from these standards that are detailed by the developers of the several synthetic covering processes. We'll enumerate those in later chapters as we discuss each synthetic covering process individually.

Pigmented dopes must be applied over the clear dopes to protect the fabric from the sunlight. Sufficient pigment must be added to the dope to form an opaque surface. Pigmented dopes consist of the properly colored pigment added to the clear dope. When an aluminum finish is desired, one gallon of the clear nitrocellulose dope is mixed with 12 ounces of aluminum powder and an equal additional amount of glycol sebacate plasticizer. Sufficient thinner is then added so that two coats of this dope will give a film weight of about two ounces per square yard. An aluminum paste is now available which makes this mixing process easier.

Panels should be doped in a horizontal position, whenever possible, to prevent the dope from running. Hand brush the first coat of dope and work it uniformly into the fabric. A minimum of 30 minutes under good atmospheric conditions should be allowed for drying between coats. Surface (finishing) tape should be applied, along with patches and reinforcements around control cable exits, etc., just prior to the second coat of dope. This second coat should also be brushed on as smoothly as possible. A third and fourth coat of clear dope can be applied by either brushing or spraying. These coats of clear dope provide a taut and rigid surface to the fabric covering. If desired, this surface may be smoothed by lightly rubbing with number 280 or 320 wet or dry sandpaper, or a similar abrasive. When being rubbed, all surfaces should be electrically grounded to dissipate static electricity. The doping is completed by spraying two or more coats of the properly colored pigmented dope on the surface.

Under certain unfavorable atmospheric conditions, a freshly doped surface will "blush." Blushing is caused by the precipitation of cellulose ester, which is caused largely by a high rate of evaporation and/or high humidity. High temperatures or currents of air blowing over the work increase the evaporation rate and increase blushing tendencies. Blushing seriously reduces the strength of the dope film, and the necessary precautions should be taken to guard against it. When a doped surface blushes, it becomes dull in spots, or white in extreme cases.

The surface under the doped fabric must be protected to prevent the dope from "lifting" the paint on the structure. A common method is to apply dope-proof paint or zinc chromate primer over all parts that come in contact with the doped fabric. Another excellent method is to cement aluminum foil (.0005 thick) to the surfaces that come in contact with the doped fabric. It is applied over the regular finish. Other materials, such as cellophane tape, have been used successfully in place of aluminum foil.

Dope Materials

Aircraft dope is any liquid applied to a fabric surface to produce tautness by shrinkage, to increase strength, to protect the fabric, to waterprooof, and to make the fabric airtight. Aircraft dopes are also used extensively in the repair and rejuvenation of aircraft fabric surfaces.

Aircraft dope is technically a colloidal solution of cellulose acetate butyrate or cellulose nitrate. If nitric acid was used in the chemical manufacturing of the dope, it is known as cellulose nitrate dope. If acetic and butyric acids were used, the dope is known as cellulose acetate butyrate dope.

Cellulose Nitrate Dope

Nitrocellulose dope is a solution of nitrocellulose and a plasticizer, such as glycol sebacate, ethyl acetate, butyl acetate, or butyl alcohol, or toluene. The nitrocellulose base is made by treating cotton in nitric acid. The plasticizer aids in producing a flexible film. Both the plasticizer and the solvents are responsible for the tautening action of dope. Thinners such as benzol or ethyl alcohol are sometimes added to the dope to obtain the proper consistency. These thinners evaporate with the volatile solvents.

Nitrate dope flows more freely and is more easily applied to fabric than butyrate dope. It burns readily and rapidly and is difficult to extinguish, whereas butyrate dope burns slowly and is easily extinguished. The tautening effect of nitrate is not quite so great as that of butyrate.

Cellulose Acetate Butyrate Dope

This type of dope is composed of cellulose acetate butyrate and a plasticizer, triphenyl phosphate, which are non-volatile when mixed with ethyl acetate, butyl acetate, diacetone alcohol or methyl ethyl ketone (MEK), all of which are volatile.

Butyrate dope has a greater tautening effect on fabric and is more fire resistant than nitrate dope. The solvents of butyrate dope are more penetrating than those of nitrate dope, and butyrate dope can be applied successfully over dried nitrate dope on a fabric surface.

Both the cellulose nitrate and cellulose acetate butyrate dopes, without the addition of color pigments, are a clear, transparent solution. Both are used on aircraft fabric covering to shrink and tighten the fabric to a drum-like surface, to impregnate and fill the fabric mesh, and to waterproof, airproof, strengthen, and preserve the fabric.

Pigments of the desired color may be added to the final two or three coats of dope applied to the fabric to attain the desired color and trim on the aircraft.

Aluminum Pigmented Dopes

When at least two or more coats of aluminum pigmented dope (brushed or sprayed) have been applied over the first two or three coats of clear dope after they have dried and have been sanded, a thin film of aluminum is formed over the fabric and the undercoats of clear dope. This aluminum film insulates the fabric from the sun's heat and reflects the heat and ultraviolet raqs away from the fabric.

Aluminum pigmented dopes may be purchased already mixed and ready for application. However, it is often more economical and desirable to mix the powdered aluminum into the clear dope in the shop.

The aluminum for mixing into the clear dope may be obtained in either powder form or paste form. In the powdered form it is nothing more than finely ground aluminum metal. In the paste form the aluminum metal has been mixed with an adhesive agent to form a putty-like paste.

Recommended mixing proportions are 1-½ pounds of aluminum powder to five gallons of clear dope, or 1-¾ pounds of aluminum paste to five gallons of clear dope. First, thoroughly mix and dissolve the powder or paste in a small amount of alcohol thinner and then add to the clear dope.

Temperature and Humidity Effects on Dope

The successful application of dope finished on fabric depends on many things, including the method of application, temperature, humidity, correct mixture of anti-blush reducers and thinners, sanding, and preparation of the fabric. In addition to the special methods necessary in the application of dope, further precautions are required in the handling, storage, and use of dope because it is flammable and its fumes are harmful if breathed in excess. For the best and safest results, doping is usually done in a special dope room where many of these factors can be controlled.

In cold weather, dopes left in unheated rooms or outside become quite viscous. Cold dope should be kept in a warm room

It is not recommended that the aircraft's surfaces be employed as a work bench.

between 75 degrees F and 80 degrees F at least 24 hours before being used. Dope in large drum containers (55 gal) will require 48 hours to reach this temperature. Cold dope will pull and rope under the brush and, if thinned sufficiently to spray or brush, will use extra thinner needlessly, and will lack body when the thinner evaporates.

Bubbles and Blisters

A heavy coat of lacquer applied over a doped surface that is not thoroughly dry will tend to form bubbles. To prevent this condition, allow the surface to dry for 10 to 12 hours. Bubbles may be removed by washing the surface with dope thinner until smooth, allowing the surface to dry, and then sanding before refinishing. Blisters are caused by dope dripping through to the opposite surface during application of the priming coat, as a result of excessive brushing over spars, ribs, or other parts. Dope may also seep through fittings, inspection openings, or patches to form blisters. Extreme care should be taken to avoid blisters inasmuch as they can be removed only by cutting the fabric at the blister and patching. When applying the prime coat of dope to fuselage fabric, newspapers spread inside the fuselage will guard against dope dripping through to an opposite surface.

Slack Panels

Slack panels are caused by loose application of the fabric, or the fabric may have been applied with proper tension but permitted to reamin undoped for too long a period, thus losing its tension. Fabric slackened by remaining undoped may be tightened by the application of acetone if it is applied as soon as the slackening is noticeable.

Extremes of temperature or humidity may cause dope to dry in such a condition that the fabric becomes slack. This can be remedied by spraying on another coat of dope containing either a slow dryer, such as butyl alcohol, or a rapid dryer, such as acetone, as conditions may require.

Inconsistent Coloring

Inconsistent coloring of enamels, paints, and pigmented dope is caused by the pigments settling to the bottom of the container, thus depriving the upper portion of the liquid of its proper proportion of pigment. If shaking the container does not distibute the pigment satisfactorily, a broad paddle or an agitator should be used to stir the mixture thoroughly.

Pinholes

Pinholes in the dope film can be caused by the temperature of the dope room being too high, by not brushing the prime coat well into the fabric to completely seal it, by a heavy spray coat of a mixture containing too much thinner, or by water, oil, or dirt in the air supply of the spray gun. Pinholes may be caused also by not allowing sufficient time for drying between coats.

Blushing

Blushing in dopes or lacquers is common in humid weather. This condition is caused by rapid evaporation of thinners and solvents. What happens is, the evaporation lowers the temperature on the surface of the freshly doped fabric, causing condensation of moisture from the atmosphere. This moisture on the surface of the wet dope or lacquer precipitates the cellulose nitrate or cellulose acetate out of solution, thus giving the thick, milky-white appearance known as blush. Of course, such a decomposed finish is of no value either in tautening or protecting the fabric for any period of time.

The common causes of blushing are:

1. Temperature too low.
2. Relative humidity too high.
3. Drafts over the freshly doped surface.
4. Use of acetone as a thinner instead of nitrate thinner.

If causes 1 and 2 can't be corrected, blushing may be avoided by adding butyl alcohol to the dope in sufficient quantity to correct the condition. Dope films that have blushed may be restored by applying another coat of dope thinned with butyl alcohol. This coat will dissolve the precipitation on the previous coat. Or, the blushed film

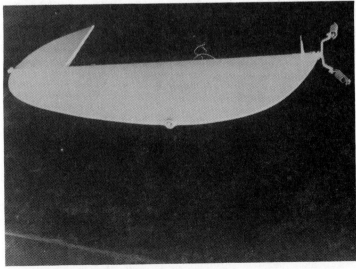

Nor is the hangar floor an ideal storage place for a newly finished rudder.

may be removed by saturating a rag with butyl alcohol and rubbing it rapidly and lightly over the blushed area. If butyl alcohol doesn't remove the bushing, acetone applied in the same way should do it. However, the best protection against blushing is to simply postpone doping operations when temperature and/or humidity conditions are unfavorable if these factors can't be controlled in the dope room. The use of large amounts of blush-retarding thinners isn't advisable because of their undesirable drying properties.

Brittleness

Brittleness is caused by applying the fabric too tightly, or by the aging of the doped surface. Over-tight panels may be loosened by spraying a 50% solution of acetone and dope over the surface to soak into the fabric layers, allowing the fabric to slacken. If the brittleness is due to age the only remedy is to re-cover the structure.

Peeling

Peeling is due to poor adhesion of the finish to the fabric and is usually caused by failure to remove moisture, oil, or grease from the fabric before it was coated. Mixing incompatible solvent systems in the finishing coats may also result in peeling.

Runs and Sags

Runs and sags in the finish are caused either by applying the dope too heavily or by allowing the dope to run over the sides and ends of the surface. Immediately after a surface is finished, the opposite and adjacent surfaces should be inspected for sags and runs.

Orange peel and pebble effect result from insufficiently thinned dope or when the spray gun is held too far from the surface.

Application Technique

First, make sure that dope and fabric materials are compatible by consulting the product manufacturer's instructions before applying finish to the aircraft surfaces. If you are not thoroughly familiar with the products to be used, it's always a good idea to finish a test sample.

Finishing materials are generally supplied at a consistency ready for brush application. For spraying operations, practically all aircraft dope, epoxy, or resin requires thinning. Avoid use of thinning agents other than those specified by the manufacturer. The amount of thinner to be used will depend on the material, atmospheric conditions, spraying equipment, the spraying technique of the operator, and the type of thinning agent employed. Thinning influences the drying time and the tautening properties of the finish, and it is necessary that it be done properly.

Apply as many coats of dope as are necessary to result in a taut and well-filled finish. A guide for finishing fabric covered aircraft as per AC 43.13 follows:

a. Two coats of clear dope, brushed on and sanded after the second coat.
b. One coat of clear dope, either brushed or sprayed, and sanded.

Ailerons are covered using same procedures as employed on wings.

c. Two coats of aluminum pigmented dope, sanded after each coat.

d. Three coats of pigmented dope of color desired, sanded and rubbed to give a smooth glossy finish when completed.

e. Care should be taken not to sand heavily over the center portion of pinked tape and over spars in order not to damage the rib-stitching cord and fabric.

Use a brush to spread the first two coats of dope uniformly on the surface. Work the dope into the fabric thoroughly, exercising care not to form an excesive film on the reverse side. The first coat should produce a thorough and uniform wetting of the fabric. To do so, work the dope with the warp and the filler for three or four brush strokes and stoke away any excess material to avoid piling up or dripping. Apply succeeding brush or spray coats with only sufficient brushing to spread the dope smoothly and evenly.

When doping fabric over plywood or metal leading edges, make sure that an adequate bond is obtained between the fabric and the leading edge. Also, when using pre-doped fabric, use a thinned dope in order to obtain a good bond betwen the fabric and the leading edge.

Apply finishing (surface) tape, drain grommets, and reinforcement patches with the second coat of dope.

Fungicidal Dope

Fungicidal dope normally is used as a first coat on cotton and linen fabric to prevent rotting. It is not needed on the synthetics. Fungicide can be purchased separately, or you can buy clear dope with the fungicide already mixed in. The fungicide zinc dimethyldithiocarbonate is recommended. Copper naphtonate is also used but may bleed through light colored finishes.

Rejuvenation of Fabric

Actually, you don't rejuvenate fabric. What you may rejuvenate is the finish. So first, determine whether or not the fabric itself is worth the cost of rejuvenating the finish.

Experience has shown that rejuvenation may at times cause fabric sag rather than tautening. When the surface to be rejuvenated has been thoroughly cleaned and the rejuvenator applied according to the manufacturer's directions, the old dope should soften through to the fabric. Cracks may then be sealed and the surface allowed to set. Finishing coats of clear and pigmented dopes can then be applied in the normal manner.

Chapter 4
Airframe Preparation

Whatever fabric covering process you choose, proper preparation and inspection of the structure before any fabric goes on is of extreme importance. You won't gain much investing in a fabric/finish job good for 15 years or more if it has to come off in a year or so to get at some rust, corrosion, deteriorating wood, or other structual problem underneath.

When re-covering a ragwing you have the opportunity to bring that airframe (and operating systems) up to like-new condition; and at today's prices—and tomorrow's!—once should be enough to re-cover your airplane. Any shop that does the job right (along with those who don't) is going to ask something over $3,000 to re-cover and finish, say, a Tri-Pacer. Therefore, if the machine is worth that investment, common sense dictates that a few extra dollars spent on airframe refurbishing before that "life-time" cover goes on is an insurance bargain.

You'll begin by removing the old fabric, of course, but don't dispose of it; you may find it quite useful as a reference later on when positioning the plastic rings for inspection plates, exit patches for rudder cables, etc. Check the inside of the old fabric for chafed spots and other tip-offs that may aid in obtaining a better re-cover job. Usually, but not always, the old fabric can be used as a guide in positioning drain grommets in the new cover. Condensed moisture inside the wings tends to collect along the trailing edges and along the rear spar ahead of ailerons and flaps—and due to dihedral, outboard of each rib. Seaplane-type grommets are also needed at low points on the belly of the airplane and beneath the rudder post.

Fuselage

Thoroughly clean the structure. Then, using a mangifying glass, inspect all welds of the steel tubing for cracks. Similarly inspect all fittings, such as those that contain control cable pulleys and attachment of the jack-screw (if installed) that controls stabilizer.

Fatigue cracks sometimes appear in steel tubing directly adjacent to a weld where the tubing tends to be more brittle due to the welding process.

The 4130 chromium-molybdenum steel tubing commonly used in fuselage construction of fabric covered aircraft is highly susceptible to rust, both inside the tubing and on its exterior. Aircraft manufacturers have used two methods to keep the tubing from rusting inside: 1) an airtight frame, and 2) linseed oil forced through the tubing after welding to provide a protective coating.

But you will, of course, take nothing for granted. Drill a few small holes in the tubing so that the interior may be flushed with hot linseed oil or paralketone. Allow the flushing liquid to drain and plug the holes with cad-plated self-tapping screws or by other means. The low points of the structure (bottom longerons), with the aircraft in normal at-rest attitude, are the obvious places to suspect internal rust. Many A&P's use an ice pick to probe for rust-weakened areas of tubing. It's crude but effective, like spitting on cylinder heads to quickly locate an engine mis-fire. Common sense is one's most useful tool whatever the job.

Steel fittings that show appreciable rust usually must be replaced. Flat steel plate is very quickly weakened by rust.

For aluminum parts, treatment includes the removal, by hand scrubbing, of as much of the corrosion as practicable, then the inhibition of residual material by chemical means, followed by the restoration of permanent surface coatings. Don't use steel wool, emery cloth, steel (except stainless steel) wire brushes, or severe abrasive cleaners because particles of the steel wool or emery cloth will become embedded in the soft surface material and promote more corrosion. Hand polishing corroded areas with household abrasives or with metal polish available under Specification MIL-P-6888 is acceptable for use on clad aluminum but must not be used on anodized aluminum since it is severe enough to actually remove the protective anodized film. If the surface is particularly difficult to clean, Type II material under Specification MIL-C-5410 mixed half and half with solvent or mineral spirits may be used. Treat any superficial corrosion with a 10 percent solution of sodium dichromate to which one percent of chromium trioxide has been added, or with a solution available under Specification MIL-C-5541. Allow these solu-

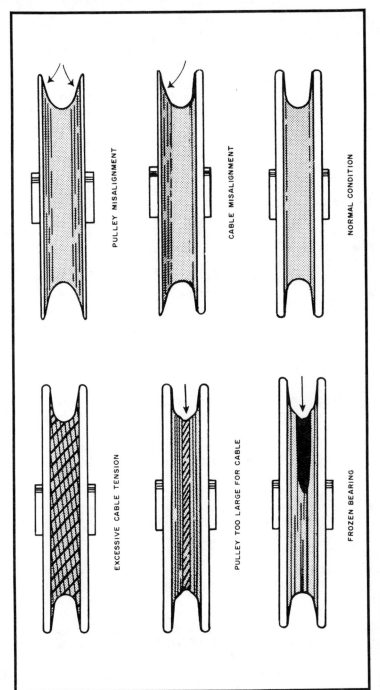

Pulley wear patterns.

tions to remain on the corroded area for five to 20 minutes and then wipe the surface dry. A more severe cleaning procedure consists of using a 10 percent solution of chromic acid to which has been added approximately 20 drops of battery electrolyte per gallon. This is, of course, the electrolyte from a lead-acid type battery. Thorough brushing with a stiff fiber brush should loosen or remove most existing corrosion and assure complete penetration of the inhibitor into crevices and pits. Allow the chromic acid to remain in place for at least five minutes, then remove the excess by flushing with water or wiping with a wet cloth. Apply a protective coating the same day that the corrosion treatment is accomplished.

When an anodized surface coating is damaged, it can only be partially restored by chemical surface treatment. Therefore, exercise care in any cleaning process to avoid unnecessary breaking of the protective film, particularly at the edges of the aluminum sheet. Chromic acid and other inhibitive treatments tend to restore the oxide film.

Chemical cleaners must be used with care whatever the structural material when cleaning an airframe. The danger of entrapping corrosive materials in faying surfaces and crevices counteracts any advantage in their speed and effectiveness. Use materials that are relatively neutral and easy to remove.

Examine the control system, noting any rusted or frayed cables, and look carefully at the bellcranks for cracks, proper alignment, and security of attachment. Rotate the pulleys to check for flat spots and insure smooth, free operation. Cables should be replaced if damaged, distorted, worn, or corroded, even though the strands are not broken.

Inspect the hydraulic lines and fittings for general condition, leaks, and security of attachment. Look for dents, kinks, and signs of chafing in the lines.

Check the electrical wiring for proper installation and security of attachment. Inspect the grommets, plastic tubing, and connectors. Determine that the solder is not deteriorated or corroded on the connections and that terminals are not dirty or misaligned. Replace wires with broken insulation.

Separate wiring from hydraulic and fuel lines. Such fluids deteriorate insulation on electrical wires, and an arcing fault in an electric line can puncture a fuel or hydraulic line and result in fire. Where wiring or wiring bundles pass through the structure or bulkheads, inspect for proper clamping of the sustaining grommets. Insure sufficient slack between the last clamp and the connector.

There are several kinds of plastic electrical tape, all of which is made from polyvinylchloride. Use only that which carries the Fire Underwriter's Laboratory (UL) approval as flame-resistant.

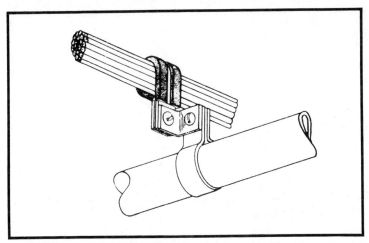

Separation of wires from plumbing lines.

The protective coating to be applied to the airframe prior to re-cover should be brushed or sprayed on the same day that the tubing is cleaned. If you are using the Stits Poly-Fiber Process, all steel components will be primed with Stits EP-420 Epoxy Primer. Since this will not "lift" in contact with fabric finishing materials, dope-proofing is not necessary.

If you are using the Ceconite or Eonnox Process, you may prime the airframe tubing with zinc chromate and then treat all parts of the structure which come in contact with doped fabric with a protective coating such as aluminum foil, dope-proof paint, or cellulose tape.

If you are re-covering with Razorback Fiberglas, an epoxy primer is recommended, such as the Stits EP-420. Again, dope-proofing isn't necessary when using this product. You can also use zinc chromate followed by dope-roof paint under Fiberglas, if you prefer.

Cover all points of the structure, such as sharp edges, bolt-heads, etc., which are likely to chafe or wear the covering with

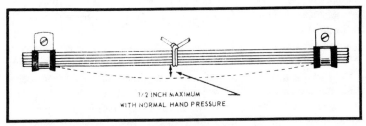

1/2 INCH MAXIMUM
WITH NORMAL HAND PRESSURE

Allowable slack in wiring bundle between supporting grommets.

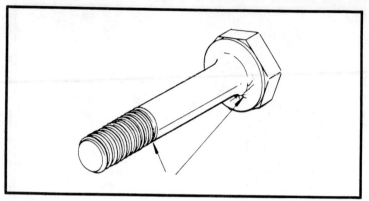

Typical bolt cracks. Inspect with a 10-power magnifying glass.

doped-on fabric strips or cover with an adhesive tape. After the cover has been installed, reinforce the chafe points by doping on fabric patches.

Wings

If the wings are metal-framed, check for corrosion and signs of distortion or unusual stress. Thoroughly clean and, using a ten-power magnifying glass, check all metal fittings, such as aileron and flap hinge brackets, strut and landing gear attach brackets, for cracks and security of attachment.

Inspect electrical wiring, hydraulic and fuel lines and connection, and fuel tank installations. Check the tanks for security of mounting and signs of leakage. Inspect the overflow and drain lines for kinks and proper routing to the outside air. Just keep in mind that it should be at least a dozen years before this structure will be "open for inspection" again.

The metal wing structure will be prime-coated as the fuselage was, depending upon the cover/finish process to be used.

Wooden wings will be inspected differently. Some of the older lightplanes have spruce spars with aluminum ribs; some are all-wood framed with wire or steel tube internal bracing; and then there are the Bellancas and early Mooneys, for example, that have plywood-covered wings.

The problem with plywood-covered wings is that they are hard to thoroughly inspect internally, and such a wing with, say, 20 years of service, has got to be suspect. It's true that aircraft-grade spruce is superior to metal in many ways and, if it can be kept free of moisture, will last just as long if not longer than a metal structure. But keeping the internal wooden-wing structure free of moisture—including hydraulic fluid, oil, grease, and gasoline, as well as

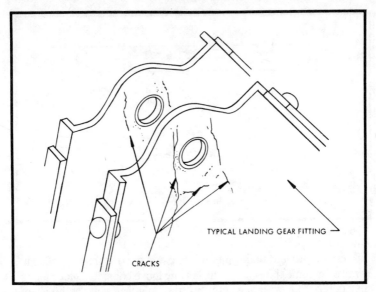

Typical cracks near bolt holes.

water—demands good ventilation and drainage along with a proper coating of protective varnish or epoxy.

Naturally, if any internal wood deterioration is suspected the plywood skin will have to come off so the wing can be thoroughly inspected and refurbished. It isn't a happy situation, because mois-

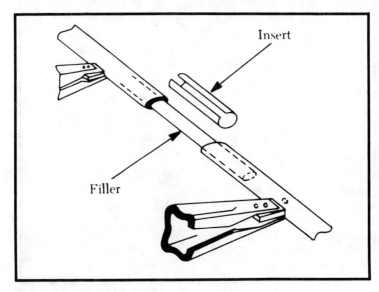

Trailing edge repair between ribs.

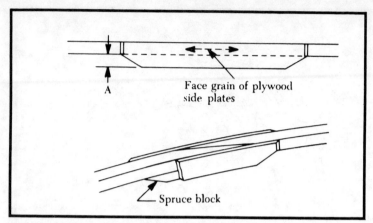

Face grain of plywood side plates

Spruce block

A rib capstrip repair.

ture can be present under metal fittings, and wood that has been in service for some time can shrink leaving loose bolts; and glued joints may deteriorate with age, etc. So, the only way you can be absolutely certain that a wood-framed wing is sound is to be able to inspect every inch of it.

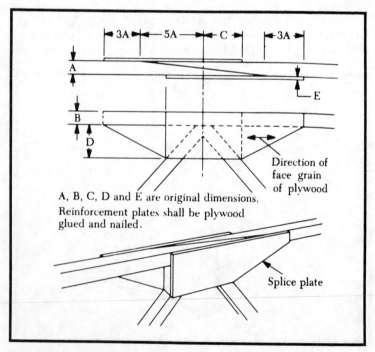

A, B, C, D and E are original dimensions.
Reinforcement plates shall be plywood glued and nailed.

Direction of face grain of plywood

Splice plate

A wooden rib repair at a joint.

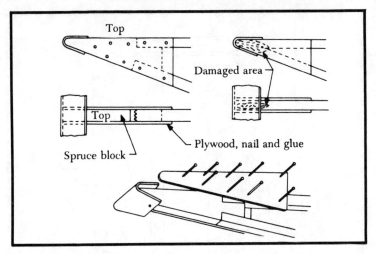

A rib tailing edge repair.

Always check both sides of the spars; look for cracks, checks, and compression damage, especially at bolt holes. All bolts should be removed for inspection. Be careful not to crush the wood by over-

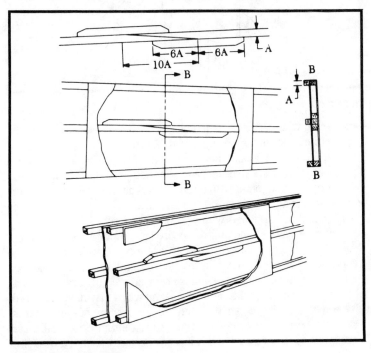

A compression rib repair.

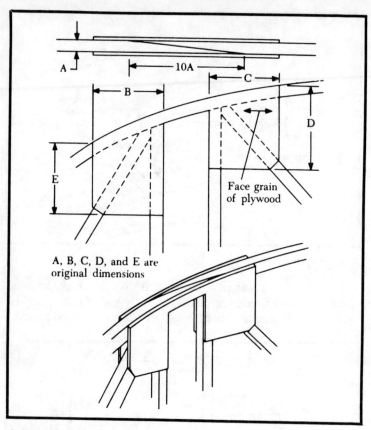

A rib repair at a spar.

tightening when replacing the bolts. It is usually best to open box-spars to check inside for signs of moisture.

Any partially-loose spar reinforcing plates should have fresh glue forced into the separation and then clamped until the glue cures.

Probe glued joints with a thin-bladed blunt-end knife; and zinc chromate all metal fittings, both steel and aluminum. All wood will be sanded and re-varnished with Marine Spar Varnish.

If internal drag and anti-drag wires are replaced, it'll be necessary to carefully square the wing. Mark exact center points at the center-line of each spar where the center lines of compression members line-up. The spars must remain exactly parallel to each other. Since some slight shrinkage of the wood may have occurred, it may be necessary to shim one end of one or more of the compression members. Do not over-tighten the drag and antiwires. All that is necessary is to have each individual bay squarely adjusted, and all of the wires as nearly the same tension as possible.

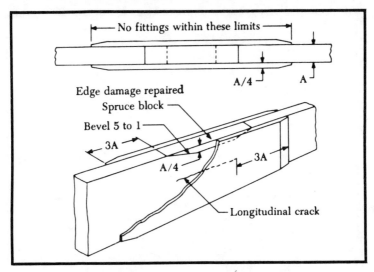

The repair of cracks and edge damage on a solid spar.

Before covering plywood skin surfaces with fabric, prepare the surface by cleaning and applying sealer and dope.

Sand all surface areas that have been smeared with glue to expose a clean wood surface. Completely remove traces of sawdust and clean any oil or grease spots by carefully washing with naptha.

After cleaning the surfaces, apply one brush coat or two dip coats (wiped) of a dope-proof sealer, such as that conforming to Mil Spec MIL-V-6894, or Stits Poly-Brush with the Stits Process, and allowed to dry. If the cloth covering is to be finished in Butyrate dope, then give the plywood surface two coats of clear dope, allowing the first coat to dry about 45 minutes before applying the second. If the Stits Process is being used, the two coats of clear dope aren't needed, as the Poly-Brush sealer provides both protection for the wood and a good adhesive base for the Poly-Fiber cloth (this process is detailed in a following chapter).

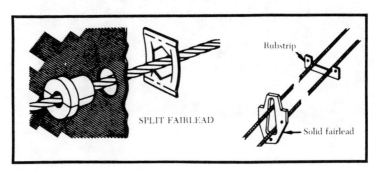

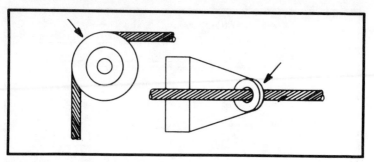

Typical breakage points.

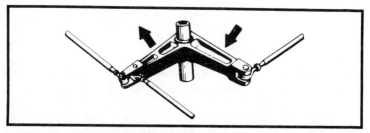

Control system bellcrank; inspect carefully.

The all-wood Viking wing is resin-dipped to seal out moisture before being covered with mahogany plywood and Dacron.

Control Surfaces

All control surfaces are, of course, removed from the wings and tail for re-covering. All welds, hinge brackets, and fittings must be inspected for cracks with a magnifying glass after they have been thoroughly cleaned. Then, these structures will receive protective coatings as did the fuselage and wings.

Since the dynamic and static balance of control surfaces may not be altered without the danger of inducing flutter, especially in high-performance aircraft, care must be taken to preserve the Center of Gravity of each control surface exactly as it was with its original cover and finish. The best way to insure this is to carefully weigh and determine the CG of each control surface *before* removing the old fabric. A simple method for establishing control surface CG is illustrated in the chapter dealing with the Ceconite Process.

Chapter 5

Stits Poly-Fiber Process

The Stits Poly-Fiber Process is detailed in the Poly-Fiber Procedure Manual No. 1, available from Stits Aircraft Coatings, P. O. Box 3084, Riverside, CA 92509, and the data offered here are taken verbatim from that manual, following brief descriptions of the products used.

Poly-Brush—used for the first two brush or spray coats and for attaching finishing tapes and reinforcement patches.

Poly-Spray—for the spray application of the third to sixth coat. Contains the correct proportions of aluminum pigment to block sunlight and fill the fabric weave.

Poly-Tone—Stits pigmented finishes for fabric and metal.

Poly-Tak—an improved fabric cement used to attach fabric to the airframe and cemented seams.

Poly-Dope Reducer—for viscosity and drying control of Poly-Brush, Poly-Spray, and Poly-Tone.

Dacron Finishing Tapes—for fabric seam reinforcement.

Adhesive Filament Tapes—for rib lacing reinforcement.

Dacron Threads—for sewing envelopes, blankets, and rib lacing.

Substitution of Original Materials

1. The original fabric will be substituted with Poly-Fiber Style D-101A, 3.7 oz weight, or Style D-103, 2.7 oz weight fabric. Fabric Style D-104, a 1.7 oz weight cloth is used over plywood surfaces.

2. The original rib lacing cord will be substituted with Poly-Fiber Dacron rib lacing cord, identified with the legend,

"Poly-Fiber, FAA PMA Stits Aircraft," stamped on the spool.

3. The original sewing threads will be substituted with Poly-Fiber Dacron sewing thread.

4. The original reinforcing tapes will be substituted with Stits special Rayon bi-directional filament reinforced adhesive tapes, ¼, ⅜, or ½-in wide…the original cotton reinforcing tape used for inter-rib bracing may also be replaced with Poly-Fiber Rayon filament reinforcing tape.

5. The original surface or "finishing" tapes will be substituted with Poly-Fiber Dacron finising tapes. Dacron tape is preferred over Grade A cotton tape for durability. Dacron also has the advantage over Fiberglas finishing tapes of being more adaptable to compound contours by heat-shrinking the excess material.

6. Poly-Brush will be used instead of clear nitrate or butyrate dope. Poly-Spray will be used instead of aluminum pigmented nitrate or butyrate dope for fabric weave fill and

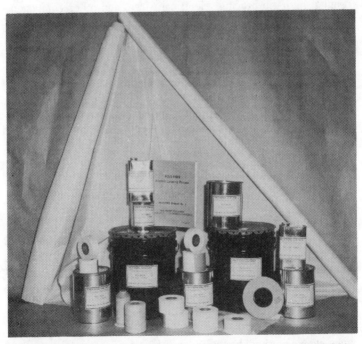

Representative packages of Stits products. Needed for re-covering and finishing a Citabria or Taylorcraft: 45 yds Poly-Fiber cloth; 36 gals Stits finishes; one gal each of Poly-Tak Cement and reducer; two rolls reinforcing tape, seven rolls finishing tape, and a spool of rib-lacing cord. At least 75% of the cost of any re-cover job is labor.

ultraviolet protection. Poly-Tone pigmented finish re-places pigmented nitrate and butyrate dope or synthetic enamel finish. Poly-Dope reducers and retarders are added when needed.

7. Where a Mil Spec fabric cement or any other fabric cement was originally used to attach the fabric to the airframe or for over-lapping seavs, an improved fabric cement, Poly-Tak, will be used. In tension tests on a one-inch over-lap D-101A Dacron-to-Dacron Poly-Tak cemented seam, the fabric always fails first. Do not re-package Poly-Tak and store in bare steel containers due to rapid degradation and loss of outstanding adhesive characteristics. Add MEK to reduce Poly-Tak viscosity when needed due to evaporation.

Preparation

Before installing fabric on any component, a check should be made of all interior structures, bolts, clevis pins, drag wires, cable routing, inter-rib bracing, electrical wires, and other components that will not be readily accessible for inspection after the fabric is installed.

All steel components should be primed with Stits EP-420 Epoxy Primer.

When covering over wood components such as ribs which are protected with a varnish which may "lift" due to the solvents in dope or fabric cement, a dope-proof paint or cellulose tape should be applied over the varnish. Stits Epoxy Primer and Varnish and Urethane Varnish will not lift and need not be protected with a dope-proof paint.

All sharp edges which the fabric will contact must be covered with a cloth masking tape to prevent cutting through the fabric.

Attaching the Fabric

The procedures outlined in the FAA Manual AC 43.13-1A & 2 (formerly CAM-18) may be used as a guide in the covering, sewing, lacing, and finishing procedure. Compliance with more stringent requirements for conventional material such as hand-sewing seams and use of 3-in and 4-in tapes on cemented seams are optional.

The Poly-Fiber fabric may be attached to the airframe in the identical manner as the original covering, usually the blanket or sewn-sleeve method; however, over-lapping cemented seams made directly on the airframe using Poly-Tak cement, or any combination of machine-sewn seams, hand-sewn seams and cemented seams may be used.

In November, 1971 Stits successfully completed an extensive test program to obtain FAA approval for Poly-Tak cemented seams in substitute for sewn seams on all aircraft regardless of the Red Line (Vne). A minimum 2-in over-lap splice, covered with a minimum 2-in wide finishing tape, may be used on any area of the wings, and a minimum 1-in over-lap splice, covered with a minimum 2-in wide finishing tape, may be used on all other parts of the airframe.

All cemented seams are to be located only over supporting airframe structures conforming to the final contour of the taut fabric cover. Cement seams are to be made by cementing the full seam width directly on the airframe—not a flat surface then transferred to

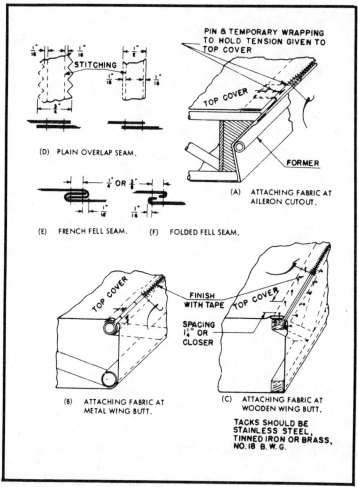

Typical methods of attaching fabric.

the airframe. No cement seams are to be located in open bay areas except when making repairs to previously finished fabric surfaces.

The following steps outline a common procedure for installation of fabric on a typical two and four-place light aircraft fuselage:

1. Sew two strips of wide fabric side by side with sufficient length to reach the full length of the fuselage section which will be covered with fabric. The sewn seam will discontinue at the start of the vertical stabilizer.

Most types of "domestic" sewing machines, properly adjusted, may be used to sew the Dacron cloth; however, upholstery or heavy duty machines are usually used.

2. Position the blanket on top of the fuselage with the seam down the center.

3. Cut and fit two pieces of fabric on each side of the vertical stabilizer, fasten with pins to the blanket and to each other up the leading edge of the stabilizer.

4. Machine sew the vertical stabilizer panels to the blanket and sew the seam at the leading edge of the vertical stabilizer.

5. Reposition the blanket on the fuselage, pin in position temporarily, and cut off the excess material extending an inch below the lower longerons.

6. Sew together side-by-side the two wedge shaped pieces which were cut from the blanket; fit them on the bottom of the fuselage, attach to the lower longerons with Poly-Tak cement.

7. Re-install the blanket on the top of the fuselage and overlap the bottom fuselage fabric a minimum of one inch at the lower longerons. Attach all other areas of the blanket to the fuselage structure with Poly-Tak fabric cement. Partially heat-shrink, then cover all cemented seams with 2-inch finishing tape and Poly-Brush. After sufficient drying, about one hour at 70 degrees F, finish the heat-shrink to full taut desired.

When gluing fabric to bare aluminum surfaces such as wing components, thoroughly clean the aluminum surface with Stits Metl-Sol #C-2200 metal cleaner and apply a coat of Poly-Tak first. (Poly-Tak provides excellent adhesion to all clean metal surfaces). After drying, the fabric is attached with Poly-Tak in the usual manner. All cemented seams are covered with 2-inch finishing tape before full tautening.

The fabric is initially installed snug or with only a few minor wrinkles showing since unfinished Dacron is capable of shrinking about 10%. A blanket stretched in one direction, but very loose in the other direction, will heat taut in the same ratio.

Shrinking the Fabric

When the Poly-Fiber has been correctly attached to the airframe, heat is applied to obtain the final desired tautness. Experience has shown that the best procedure is to tauten the fabric in several increments of heat increase, rather than apply a high temperature to obtain the final tautness on the first application. An ordinary household iron, with a thermostat control, is the most common source of heat.

The first heat application is made with a setting of 225 to 250 degrees F, or with the temperature indicator setting on "Rayon" or slightly above. After the entire surface has been "levelled" or pulled snug with all the winkles removed, the temperature is increased to a setting for "Wool," or about 350 degrees F, and the operation repeated. The iron is continually moved over the surface of the fabric at a rate of four to seven inches per second. Experience will determine the best procedure. A slower iron movement may be neces-

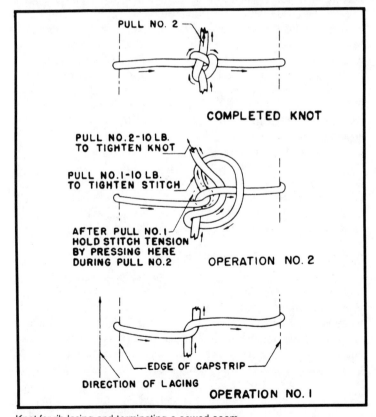

Knot for rib lacing and terminating a sewed seam.

sary over leading edges and other structural members where a "heat sink" is caused by the proximity of the cloth to the members. Do not overheat, because the fabric will start to deteriorate above 400 degrees F.

To avoid the possibility of cemented seam slippage when the fabric is attached with cement instead of sewn seams, the fabric is only partially tautened, then all seams covered with a 2-inch finishing tape. Those fabric seam areas which will be covered with a finishing tape should have one Poly-Brush coat, dried, before tape application, to provide a good bonding surface. After the cement and Poly-Brush has dried sufficiently, the tautening procedure is completed.

There are no specifications for determining the correct tension for aircraft fabric. The fabric should be sufficiently tight to be stable in the slipstream, but not tight enough to distort the structure. Generally, fabric tight enough to bounce a coin (quarter) is considered satisfactory. Since Poly-Dope is a non-tautening formula, it will not tauten the fabric after application.

Fabric pulled only wrinkle-free, not taut, will lack the desired tension after all coatings have been applied. Cold weather will also cause marginally-taut fabric to show wrinkles. It is permissible to further heat and tauten the fabric at any stage of the coating buildup and even after the final Poly-Tone finish. To reduce damage to the coating, a damp cotton cloth is used over the iron. However, we recommend that all the tautening be done on the bare fabric for best appearance.

Dacron fabric on an open airframe will not shrink further from the direct sunlight in the hottest climate. However, in exceptional cases, sufficiently high temperatures to cause localized shrinking of previously unshrunk Dacron finishing tapes may be induced on black painted fabric surfaces over metal components or surfaces covered with black protective plastic, stored in direct sunlight in hot climates.

Application of First Poly-Brush Coat

After the Poly-Fiber has been heat-shrunk according to the recommended procedure, brush or spray on one coat of Poly-Brush with good penetration. Spray application is the preferred procedure to avoid brush marks showing after the finish coat. Brushing technique is approximately the same as with conventional nitrate or butyrate dope. The first brush coat should be sufficiently wet to penetrate the fabric; however, not excessive to cause dripping from the opposite side. A hog hair or horse hair brush is preferred over a Nylon brush for more even dispersement. Agitate thoroughly and often to disperse the white pigment. Drying time of Poly-Brush at brushing viscosity will be approximately 45 minutes at 70 degrees F. Dust-free time is 10 to 15 minutes.

Spray Gun Application of Poly-Brush

Poly-Brush is packaged in the correct viscosity for brush application to accomodate the installation of the finishing tapes, reinforcing patches, and the covering of plywood surfaces. For spray gun applications, reduce Poly-Brush at an approximate ratio of three parts to one part Poly-Dope Reducer, either R-65-75, or RR-8500, depending on the temperature.

The first spray coat should be applied working small areas with several cross coats, applied one immediately after the other, until the fabric is saturated and the dope no longer sinks into the fabric weave, but leaves a wet gloss on the surface. This requires two to four passes with the spray gun and will be equivalent to the first brush coat.

Some brands of spray guns may tend to cobweb the Poly-Brush when thinned only three to one. This can be remedied by further thinning when necessary.

Drying time of Poly-Brush reduced to spray viscosity will be approximately one hour at 70 degrees F. Dust-free time is 10 to 15 minutes.

Rib Lacing

After the first coat of Poly-Brush has dried, the filament reinforcing tapes, the same width as the ribs, are positioned on top of the

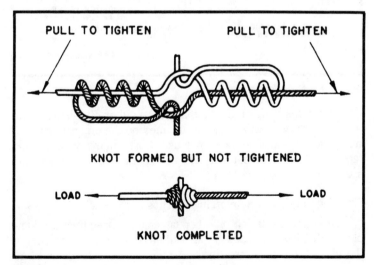

Splice knot.

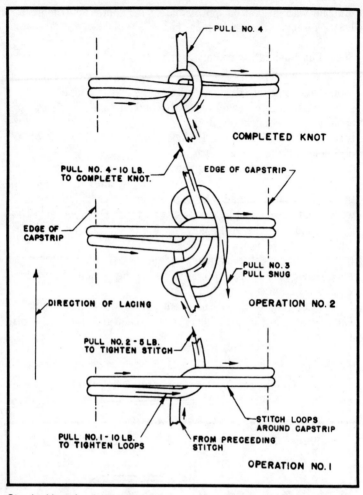

Standard knot for double loop lacing.

ribs, continuosly over the area that will be either rib-stitched, secured with screws, wire clips, or any method the original manufacturer used. Control surfaces may use short lengths of reinforcing tape at each stitch or fastener. The correct rib lacing procedure and spacing are detailed in AC 43.13-1A & 2.

Finishing Tapes and Reinforcing Patches

After the rib lacing or other fastening procedures are completed, the finishing tapes are applied on all seams, sharp edges of the aircraft components, ribs and other areas such as fuselage stringers that may need reinforcing to prevent chafing or wearing through during service. Tapes are centered on the outside edge of the over-lap on cemented seams and on the middle of sewn seams.

Reinforcing patches are cut from Dacron cloth with pinking shears and installed around wing fittings and other objects or holes through the fabric.

The width of the finishing tapes used will depend on the location. Two-inch width is normally used on all sewn seams and over wing and control surface ribs. One-inch width is more economical over fuselage stringers where no stitching or seams are located. Minimum 2-inch width may also be used on all over-lapping cemented seams including spanwise seams on wing leading and trailing edges. Wider tapes are optional.

A coat of Poly-Brush is applied to the surface first and the tapes laid immediately over the wet dope. A second coat is then brushed through to wet the tapes. Work one rib or section at a time, position the tapes straight and brush out all bubbles before going on to the

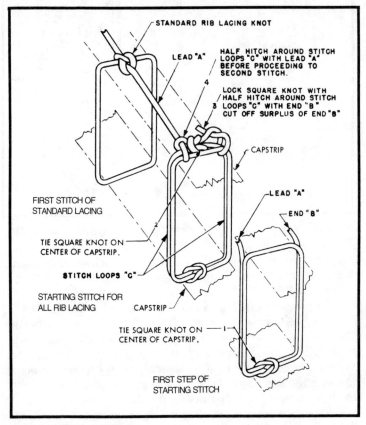

STANDARD RIB LACING KNOT

LEAD "A"

HALF HITCH AROUND STITCH LOOPS "C" WITH LEAD "A" BEFORE PROCEEDING TO SECOND STITCH.

4

LOCK SQUARE KNOT WITH HALF HITCH AROUND STITCH LOOPS "C" WITH END "B" CUT OFF SURPLUS OF END "B"

3

CAPSTRIP

FIRST STITCH OF STANDARD LACING

LEAD "A"

END "B"

TIE SQUARE KNOT ON CENTER OF CAPSTRIP.

2

STITCH LOOPS "C"

STARTING STITCH FOR ALL RIB LACING

CAPSTRIP

TIE SQUARE KNOT ON CENTER OF CAPSTRIP.

1

FIRST STEP OF STARTING STITCH

Starting stitch for rib stitching.

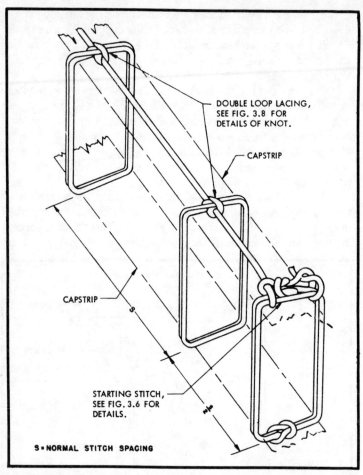

DOUBLE LOOP LACING, SEE FIG. 3.8 FOR DETAILS OF KNOT.

CAPSTRIP

CAPSTRIP

STARTING STITCH, SEE FIG. 3.6 FOR DETAILS.

S = NORMAL STITCH SPACING

Standard double loop lacing. Recommend that knot be rotated to the side of the rib.

next tape. When the dope dries too fast due to high air temperature, the drying time may be slowed by thinning with Poly-Dope Retarder Reducer, RR-8500.

Do not use butyrate or nitrate dope to apply the finishing tapes.

Long sections of tape are applied in a straight line by attaching about two inches of one end, allowing it to dry, and then pull the tape with slight tension for final application. Tapes which zig-zag down ribs or stringers are the result of applying the tape a short section at a time. Any rough edges of tapes may be smoothed and levelled with the iron tip after the Poly-Brush has dried.

Tapes are pulled to a compound curve, as around the top of a rudder, fin, wingtip bow, by attaching one end first, allowing it to dry, and then stretching the tape tightly around the curved section to eliminate excess material at the tape edges. Any excess at the edges that cannot be stretched out may be removed with an iron after the Poly-Brush is dry. Poly-Brush is then worked under the loose section for adequate adhesion.

Installation of Drain Grommets and Inspection Rings

The drain grommets, inspection rings, and other reinforcing patches should be installed before the application of the second coat of Poly-Brush.

Inspection rings, drain grommets, and any other plastic reinforcing accessories, which are usually of unknown, unstable and varied chemical composition, should be installed with a good general purpose adhesive such as Goodyear Pliobond to assure permanent adhesion. Follow the manufacturer's recommendations for proper use. Drain grommets should be installed on the bottom surfaces in every location of the entire aircraft structure in which water could possibly be trapped during a normal stored attitude.

Drain holes should alwaqs be cut through the fabric (or pierced with a heated rod) when the aircraft is first put into operation. Seaplane grommets, which have an aft-facing protuding lip, are used instead of flat drain grommets in those areas which are likely to be splashed when taxiing through water or on aircraft converted to seaplane operations.

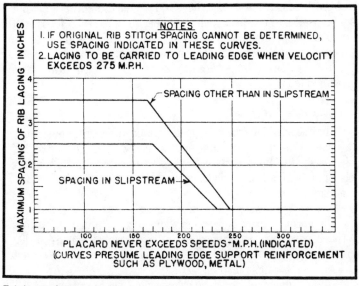

Fabric attachment spacing.

Inspection access plate reinforcing rings should be installed on the fabric adjacent to every control bellcrank, drag wire junction, cable guide or pulley, wing fitting, or any other component which must be regularly inspected during the life of the aircraft. Inspection access holes need not be opened until needed; however, all covers should be finished in matching colors and trim lines and stored.

Second Coat Poly-Brush

It is important that all pinholes through the fabric and the tapes be filled with the second coat application. The second coat should be applied only after the first coat has dried. Applying the second coat over a partially dried first coat will trap solvents and may result in bubbles or blisters appearing in the second coat. Fast drying with heat lamps will also cause bubbles due to escaping solvents being trapped.

The second coat is applied over the tapes and the entire fabric area by brushing in the opposite direction to the first coat or several cross coats by spray gun. If applying the second coat of Poly-Brush with a brush, do not continue brushing until the dope "ropes" and starts to dry. Thin with Poly-Dope Reducer when necessary due to fast drying time. Spread evenly and leave it to dry without further working, otherwise, a very rough finish with all brush marks showing will result.

The second brush coat application should provide a gloss to the fabric equivalent to about six coats of nitrate or butyrate dope. A third brush coat is not usually necessary over the entire area, but may be used in those areas which appear to be starved for lack of even dope dispersement. The entire covering area should have a gloss with no pinholes or "raw" fabric showing.

If all Poly-Brush is applied with a spray gun, a third spray coat is recommended.

First Coat Poly-Spray

After all finishing tapes, inspection rings, drain grommets, etc., are installed and the fabric sufficiently sealed with the second coat of Poly-Brush, the Poly-Spray is applied with a spray gun. Applying Poly-Spray with a brush will leave rough streaks and is not recommended.

Poly-Spray is supplied in the correct consistency and drying time for normal spray application. The mixture must be stirred thoroughly and often during application to provide an even dispersement of the various ingredients. Filter through a 44 × 60 paint strainer cone for best results.

When high air temperature causes the Poly-Spray coat to dry too fast for a "wet" coat application, the drying time may be slowed with Poly-Dope Retarder Reducer RR-8500. Do not use nitrate dope or lacquer thinner in Poly-Dope because it is not compatible and may cause a "kick-out." Drying time of Poly-Spray is approximately one hour at 70 degrees F. Dust-free time is 10 to 15 minutes.

The first cross coat of Poly-Spray is applied wet in wide, even, over-lapping passes, working the normal three to four-foot strokes from a stationary position (a cross coat is one coat applied with over-lapping passes in one direction, followed by another coat with strokes 90-degrees to the first coat).

The first Poly-Spray coat will punctuate all the roughness and flaws in the Poly-Brush application.

Sanding

After the first coat of Poly-Spray has dried sufficiently for sanding (thirty minutes to two hours, depending on the weather), the surface is wet-sanded with 280 grit sandpaper.

Poly-Brush is formulated for excellent adhesion and flexibility and does not sand easily. It is intended that all sanding for a smooth finish base be done during the Poly-Spray buildup.

Do not sand over screw heads, rib lacing, or any other sharp edges which will likely cut through the fabric. The high points and rough areas of the previously applied Poly-Brush will be removed on the first sanding. If pinholes or other irregularities are noted after the first sanding, additional Poly-Brush may be applied to those areas which previously were overlooked.

After each sanding operation is completed, the sanding residue is washed from the surface, not allowed to dry, because wiping the dry surface does not remove all residue. Use only clean rags, not rags that have been used to apply auto polish, windshield cleaner, or any silicone materials.

Poly-Spray Buildup

Sand the last coat very lightly and avoid sanding near the sharp edge of ribs and stringers due to the possibility to cutting through all the Poly-Spray coats and exposing the underlying fabric.

For a good fabric-weave fill, three to four coats of Poly-Spray are recommended on D-103 fabric, and four to six cross coats on D-101A fabric. A minimum of three coats is required to block the ultraviolet rays from the sun and provide a base for the pigmented finish coat. The amount of filling and sanding will depend on the quality of finish the mechanic is trying to obtain. However, we do not recommend to continue filling until the grain of the fabric is no longer visible when observed from an angle of about 45-degrees. A thick coat buildup of any material is more likely to pull apart when stretched across a sharp object such as the edge of capstrips. Poly-Brush, Poly-Spray, and Poly-Tone do not "crack," but may pull apart when subjected to a tight bending radius over a sharp object.

Poly-Tone Pigmented Finish Coats

Poly-Tone is considered to be the standard finish for the Poly-Fiber covering process. Stits Aero-Thane is recommended when an ultra-high gloss, more durable, solvent resistant as well as chemical resistant finish is desired. Instructions for Aero-Thane application (a two-part polyurethane enamel) are printed on the labels, as are instructions for the use of all Stits products, but we'll include them on a following page.

The application of Poly-Tone—a one-part, high-gloss, air drying flexible paint available in more than 80 colors—is similar to other conventional finishes. Do not spray in direct sunlight on a hot day or in adverse weather. The fresh coat must remain "wet" for a few minutes to flow out and provide a gloss surface. This material must be atomized to a fine mist. Using an improper spray gun or adjustment, or too heavy a viscosity, will cause cobwebbing and a rough "orange peel" surface. (See the discussion on spraying equipment which follows.)

Poly-Tone Thinning and Preparation

Poly-Tone Aircraft Finish is packaged ready for spray gun application in temperatures up to approximately 75 degrees F. For application in temperatures in the 85 to 100-degree range, reduce approximately three parts Poly-Tone to one part Poly-Dope Retarder Reducer RR-8500. Good flow out at temperatures above 100 degrees F without further reducing is difficult and not recommended. Use Poly-Dope Reducer R-65-75 when thinning is necessary due to solvent evaporation from an open container in normal 65 to 75-degree F weather. In humid or adverse weather add Poly-Flow Blush-Retarder #BR-8600 as needed to prevent blushing. One to four liquid ounces per gallon average. Any other reducer or retarder may cause the vehicle or pigments to "kick out" or alter their characteristics.

Stir thoroughly and filter through a 48 × 60 mesh paint cone before using. Color separation in storage is normal. Close the container after each use.

Poly-Tone Drying Time

Poly-Tone dries dust-free in 20 minutes at 70 degrees F. However, the film is still soft and may be marked with finger pressure up to one hour drying.

Allow 12 hours drying before using masking tape. Taping over the soft coats may leave permanent tape marks. Remove masking tapes soon after the last coat of Poly-Tone has dried dust-free for a clean finish film shear line.

As a rule of thumb, the drying time of most air drying coatings is cut in half at each 10-degree increase in temperature, and doubled at each 10-degree decrease in temperature. Temperature and humidity conditions should be taken into consideration when using any evaporating-type coating.

Poly-Tone Application

After the last coat of Poly-Spray has dried a minimum of two hours, spray a minimum of three cross coats of Poly-Tone, allowing approximately two hours drying time between coats. Three cross coats are recommended as a minimum film thickness for protection and service life.

When an exceptionally smooth finish is planned, preparation should begin with the application of the Poly-Spray. Four to six coats of the Poly-Spray may be used, with each coat lightly wet-sanded with 280 grit Wet-R-Dry paper.

A total of three to five coats of Poly-Tone finish is then applied, wet-sanding each coat except the last with 400 grit paper after drying sufficiently to produce a suitable sanding residue. Wash the sanding residue off with clean water and dry with a clean cloth. Clean the surface with a "Tac" rag just before applying the next coat.

To prevent solvent penetration through the masking tape and etching the fresh underlying Poly-Tone finish or trim colors seeping under tape edges when applying trim colors, use good quality solvent-resistant masking tape, 3M #236 or equivalent.

Poly-Tone metallic finishes are applied in light, uniform coats, wet enough to form a film but not heavy enough to flow. Any run or flow of the wet film will obliterate the metallic effect. Wet coats allow the aluminum pigments to settle deeper into the film before drying, and produce a darker, stronger color. A dryer coat traps the aluminum pigments near the surface and produces a lighter more metallic color.

The spray gun head is held a distance of six to eight inches from the surface for standard coatings and pigmented finishes, and 10 to 12 inches for metallic-pigmented finishes. It is expected that the mechanic will have some experience with the proper use of spraying equipment.

Spraying Equipment

Spraying equipment which is rated for application of lacquer, nitrate or butyrate dope, synthetic enamel and shellac, may be used to apply Poly-Brush, Poly-Spray, and Poly-Tone finish.

A DeVilbiss Model #MBC-510 or JGA-501 spray gun with #30 air cap and EX tip and needle at 50 pounds pressure has been tested satisfactorily. Any alternate brand with equivalent air cap and needle size, either pressure pot or syphon type, will also provide satisfactory service. Correct adjustment of air-to-liquid ratio is important.

Pressure pot painting equipment may apply up to twice the amount of material as the suction type gun on each coat. This should be taken into consideration when counting the number of coats applied to a surface. Ten pounds of air on the pressure pot with 50 pounds at the gun will apply about the same amount in two coats as the suction gun will in three coats.

Poly-Dope Reducer, nitrate dope and lacquer thinner, or MEK may be used to clean the spray equipment.

Due to possibility of eye damage, special attention should be given to protecting the eyes from splashing liquids when working with any coating or chemical. A plastic eye shield is recommended. A face filter mask is also recommended when spray painting to protect the lungs from spray mist.

Persons allergic to paint mist or various solvent vapors should use a head shield or hood with a fresh air supply from the air hose. Various tyes and brands are available from industrial supply stores.

Metal Surfaces

Strip the old finish and thoroughly clean with Scotch abrasive pads or fine aluminum wool. Any aluminum surface corrosion, indicated by discoloring and scaling, should be treated with E-2310 or E-2311 Phosphoric acid etch and brightener, and scrubbed to show new metal. Treat all aluminum surfaces with Aluma-Dyne E-2300 chromic acid conversion coating before the surfaces become contaminated. Apply Stits EP-420 Epoxy Primer before the chromic acid treated surfaces become contaminated. Apply the selected finish coats, Poly-Tone, Aero-Thane, or Aluma-Thane before the primed surfaces have become contaminated.

Stits Aero-Thane Enamel

Aero-Thane is a tough and flexible, high gloss, two-part polyurethane enamel formulated especially for fabric-covered aircraft surfaces and marine surfaces subjected to flexing loads. It is recommended for use over Poly-Fiber covering materials, and all primed metal and Fiberglas components of fabric-covered aircraft. It may also be used to finish suitably rejuvenated nitrate or butyrate fabric surfaces and sound synthetic enamel on fabric and metal surfaces. All cracked, peeling, or brittle synthetic enamel finish should be removed.

Aero-Thane is mixed by adding one part catalyst to three parts enamel base (one qt to ¾-gal), stirred thoroughly. Then 10 to 20% reducer is added to reduce to spray viscosity. Additional reducer may be required in warm weather for a good flow out.

Aero-Thane Enamel is applied with a spray gun in the same manner as a conventional enamel finish. Apply a light, wet tack coat and follow with two medium cross coats at 10 to 20-minute intervals to avoid runs. Dry film thickness should be 1.7 mils (.0017).

Stits Aluma-Thane Enamel

Aluma-Thane is a tough, hard, high-gloss two-part polyurethane enamel formulated for all metal and Fiberglas surfaces.

Mixing and use of Aluma-Thane is similar to the procedures employed with Aero-Thane Enamel.

Covering Over Plywood Surfaces

When covering over large areas of plywood structures, brush two coats of Poly-Brush—reduced two parts Poly-Brush to one part Poly-Dope Reducer—on the clean, bare wood surface first to assure good adhesion. Poly-Brush should be used as a wood sealer and preservative only on the outer surface which will be covered with fabric. A good grade spar varnish should be used on all other areas of wood structures. Old plywood surfaces should be stripped to bare wood, sanded and thoroughly cleaned for best results.

The choice of the weight of fabric to be installed over plywood surfaces will depend on the particular aircraft and design of the structure. On those designs which have only a leading edge or "D" section covered with plywood and the aft section covered with fabric (for example, the Culver Cadet and Mooney M-18), the heavier style D-103 or D-101A should be used because the fabric across the open areas will carry air loads and must be at least equivalent to the original Grade A cotton covering. Fabric style D-104 may be used on aircraft structures that are covered entirely with plywood (for example, Fairchild PT-26 wings and Bellanca 14-13 wings). The fabric carries no air load and acts only as weather protection for the underlying plywood.

Those structures that are only partially covered with plywood may be re-covered using an envelope or a blanket in the same manner as the original procedure. Generally, the procedure is the same as any open frame section.

On solid plywood surfaces the fabric may be applied in strips or sections in either direction. Each fabric panel is positioned and attached around all sides using Poly-Tak Cement with about one-inch wide wetted area. Adjoining strips of fabric may be over-lapped about ½-inch and, after drying, cut through with a razor blade and straight-edge to match the fabric ends. This hairline joint is later covered with a one-inch finishing tape.

Fabric over solid plywood components is ironed only enough to remove wrinkles and creases. Dampening the fabric first or using a steam iron will aid in removing creases at a lower temperature without corresponding shrinkage.

After the center area of each fabric panel has been heat-shrunk only enough to remove the wrinkles, the first coat of Poly-Brush is applied. Brush through to soften the underlying coat of Poly-Brush and adhere the fabric to the plywood surface. Work from one side across the panel to remove all bubbles by brushing them ahead and out through the un-doped fabric.

Excessively tight fabric will tend to raise out of the low areas of old plywood wing panels. A second pass with the brush about 30 seconds after first wetting the underlying dope will provide adhesion to hold the fabric down in the low areas. After the first coat is dry, a second coat is brushed or sprayed to fill the fabric to a gloss surface.

When applying the second coat by brush, do not continue working an area until the dope begins to dry and rope or a rough finish will result.

When Poly-Brush dries too fast due to high temperatures, reduce with Poly-Dope Reducer or Retarder and work smaller areas.

Two good cross coats of Poly-Spray on D-104 and three good cross coats on D-103 and D-101A weight fabric with light sanding are recommended for minimum ultraviolet protection and weave fill on plywood surfaces. Additonal coats and sanding for a smoother finish base is optional.

Poly-Tone finishes are applied in the same manner and quantity as on other fabric areas. Drying time will be slower because the solvents may escape in only one direction.

Repairs

Patches with Dacron cloth are made by thoroughly cleaning the old surface and over-lapping all edges at least two inches using Poly-Tak Cement for adhesion. Nitrate and butyrate dope and all fabric cements tested will not provide the necessary bond to Stits coatings. Removal of the old Poly-Tone pigmented finish is optional. MEK, acetone, or Poly-Dope Reducer will soften and dissolve the film. After the Poly-Tak has dried sufficiently, heat is applied to tauten the new material. Then the buildup and finish is identical to the original Poly-Fiber Process. Poly-Tone finish may be polished with rubbing compound (DuPont #101S or equivalent) to blend refinished localized areas after drying 48 hours. Wax polish may be applied after 20 days.

Refinishing Poly-Tone

Poly-Tone may be refinished when the need occurs by thoroughly cleaning off all wax, dirt and silicone using Stits C-2210 Paint Surface Cleaner. Sand with 400 grit Wet-R-Dry paper, and spray on three coats of RJ-1200 Rejuvenator. Refinish with Poly-Tone, Aero-Thane, etc., according to instructions on Rejuvenator label.

Time Lapse Covering

The best results with the Poly-Fiber covering Process will be obtained when the complete system is finished over a period not exceeding several months without exposing the Poly-Brush and Poly-Spray to the elements. Partial completion and storage of unfinished components up to a year without exposure should not present a technical problem. However, all recommended coats of Poly-Tone or any finish coats should be completed if started. The surfaces should be thoroughly cleaned with Stits C-2210 Paint Surface Cleaner before the remaining portion of the coating process continues.

Coverage

One gallon of Poly-Brush will cover approximately 150 sq ft with one brush coat or one spray cross coat. One gallon of Poly-Spray will cover approximately 200 sq ft with one good cross coat. One gallon of Poly-Tone will cover approximately 200 sq ft with one good cross coat. These amounts will vary depending on the brushing and spraying technique of the individual mechanic.

Here is a guide for materials needed to cover an average two-place airplane such as a J-3 Cub, Citabria, Taylorcraft, Champion, Porterfield, Funk, etc:

45 yds D-101A 67-in fabric	2 rolls ½-in reinforcing tape
10 gals Poly-Brush	1 gal Poly-Tak Cement
13 gals Poly-Spray	24 ea inspection rings
7 rolls 2-in finishing tape	1 box drain grommets
1 spool rib lacing cord*	1 gal Poly-Dope Reducer
13 gals Poly-Tone	(increase to 4 gals if Poly-Brush is to be sprayed)

---

*Delete rib lacing for those model aircraft that use wire clips or screws instead of lacing cord.

If the fabric material is to be sewn into a blanket, add a 4-oz spool of Dacron machine sewing thread and delete 2 qts of Poly-Tak.

Stits Aircraft will provide a complete materials list for any aircraft upon inquiry; and Stits Poly-Fiber envelopes are available from Hower Aircraft Supply, 4822 N. Royal Palm Ave., Sarasota, Florida 33580, or from Hower Aviation, 914 Verdale Dr., Spearfish, South Dakota 57783.

Tips and Suggestions

1. During the various sanding and spray operations, one should be aware of any adjacent work in progress, such as engine or parts spray cleaning or machines in operation, which would deposit fine droplets of oil, engine exhaust, solvents, chemicals or dirt on the fabric surface. Contamination of the finish is a common cause of "fisheyes," pinholes, and bubbles, which may appear in any spray coat and is often blamed on the material rather than careless workmanship.

2. An adequate water trap should be installed in the air line to eliminate the possiblility of moisture being mixed with the spray coat. Moisture will cause pinholes and blisters.

3. Do not try to spray paint in the following conditions: drafty, windy, or dusty areas; outdoors in direct sunlight if the weather is hot; outdoors in a heavy fog or if dew is forming; high humidity; below 60 degrees F or above 100 degrees F.

4. The components being re-covered and finished should not be used as a work-bench or catch-all for greasy tools between the application of the various coats.

5. Immediately before spraying each coat, the surface should be cleaned with a Tack rag to remove all lint and dust.

6. Any grease or oil accidently deposited on the surface should be removed with a clean, lint-free rag dampened with C-2210 Paint Surface Cleaner. Do not use engine cleaning solvent or gasoline because they leave a film.

7. Shop towels furnished by towel rental services may be contaminated with silicone, which transfers to the surface being cleaned with the solvent. Use new, un-treated knit-type lint-free polishing cloth available from any automobile supply store.

8. Do not wipe fresh Poly-Tone surfaces with a rag dampened in Toluol or reducers. These will mar the finish. Use C-2210 Cleaner.

9. Do not try to wipe off fresh "runs" in the Poly-Tone finish. The entire film down to the fabric may be soft and lift off. Allow any runs to dry, and then sand smooth.

10. Do not stack fresh-finished surfaces in contact with one another. They will bond together and mar the finish.
11. Do not use cold drink paper cups coated with wax, or any other contaminated container to transfer, measure, or store the various coatings. Contamination will result in pinholes, fisheyes, or poor adhesion. A small metal kitchen ladle, available from a local variety store, is recommended for transferring liquids from a round gallon can rather than trying to pour from the side.
12. Solvent penetration through to the fabric cement from heavy, repeated coats when working at low temperatures could cause slippage of cemented seams and loss of fabric tension. Heavy coats, with insufficient drying between coats, in accordance with weather conditions, should be avoided.
13. Use only good quality solvent-resistant masking tape (3M #236 or equivalent) when taping trim lines to avoid penetration through tapes and seep of trim colors under tape edges.
14. First-time users of the Poly-Fiber Process (or any process) should complete a small component through a suitable finish to gain needed experience before starting the wings or fuselage.

Almost all the problems with the use of materials requiring some skill are caused by failure to read and follow simple instructions. Remember, craftsmanship is about 95% of the ingredients in an outstanding aircraft covering job.

FAA Approval

The Poly-Fiber Covering Process was issued Supplemental Type Certificate No. SA1008WE for the prototype aircraft. The same STC number will apply to all additional aircraft and gliders covered with the Poly-Fiber process.

To simplify the procedure of adding additional aircraft to the Master Eligibility List, the FAA has provided a modified form 8100-1 (formerly 1257) which contains complete instructions to the inspectors in the field. Any aircraft covered with the Stits Poly-Fiber Process that is not already on that list may be added by having the local FAA inspector make an inspection of conformity to the Stits Manual No. 1, and fill out two copies of Form 8100-1. After the aircraft is inspected and passed, it may be put back into service immediately. All aircraft which were manufactured under the same Type Certificate Number are thereafter returned to service after processing only the usual FAA Form 337, necessary on any major repair or re-cover job.

All of the Stits covering materials with the exception of the pigmented finishes are manufactured or processed under an FAA parts manufacturer approval (PMA). The FAA does not exercise jurisdiction over pigmented finishes.

Due to the continuous up-dating of the Stits Master Eligibility List, which by this time covers almost all fabric-covered aircraft, you may want to write to Stits and inquire whether the machine you are working on has already been added to this list.

Refinishing Nitrate and Butyrate on Dacron with Stits Poly-Dopes

First, test the fabric to make sure that it is still airworthy and economically feasible to refinish considering the remaining service life.

Adhesion of the old coatings should be spot-checked with a strip of masking tape pulled off rapidly at 90-degrees. All loose sections should be stripped off. Loose or deteriorated finishing tapes, and reinforcing and inspection accessories are replaced or repaired. Use only Dacron finishing tapes attached with Poly-Brush.

If all the old nitrate and butyrate coatings will "dry strip" to the bare Dacron fabric, the buildup procedure will be identical to that when starting with new fabric. However, the fabric should be re-tautened if it appears to be slack because Poly-Dope coatings will not increase fabric tension as will nitrate and butyrate. Use a damp cloth over the hot iron to lessen the possibility of igniting any nitrate dope remaining in the fabric weave.

If the old coatings are sound and only refinishing is needed, then proceed in the followng manner:

1. Wash the surfaces with one part XOFF-310 to twenty parts clean water to remove dirt and loose oxidation.
2. Wipe with clean cloth dampened with Stits C-2210 Cleaner to remove any trace of silicone, wax, and oil. Use only new untreated knot-type lint-free polishing cloth, or equivalent paper wipe towels.
3. Wet-sand the surface with 280 grit Wet-R-Dry sandpaper and wash the residue off with clean water.
4. Apply two heavy spray coats of butyrate dope rejuvenator. Thorough penetration and softening of the dope film is important. Avoid rejuvenation in temperatures above 80-degrees F due to rapid evaporation of the solvents.
5. After the rejuvenated surfaces have dried to a firm film, two coats of Poly-Spray may be applied if the surface condition warrants additional filling or sunlight blockage for fabric protection. If small cracks in the old finish are visible after the Poly-Spray coat has dried to touch, they may be

sealed with Poly-Spray using a small soft brush. Applying additional coats of Poly-Spray and sanding with 400 grit paper after each coat has dried is optional and will depend on the surface condition.

6. Poly-Tone finish may be applied as soon as the rejuvenator and Poly-Spray has dried print free. Aero-Thane finish should not be applied until the new surface has thoroughly dried 48 hours to one week, depending on the temperature. If slow solvents in the rejuvenator (or any coating) are trapped under solvent-resistant catalyzed finish coating, there is a possibility of small blisters forming later under the finish coat in areas over metal structure such as wing leading edges and large structural tube or stringer areas. Trapped solvent vapors will escape through the backside of the surface in open fabric areas. Heat lamps or direct hot sun rays to accelerate drying of any coating can also generate vapor blisters.

Refinishing Old Pigmented Butyrate Dope Over Poly-Fiber Materials

Excessive, heavy coats of full tautening brands of pigmented butyrate dope applied (contrary to Stits' procedure) over Poly-Fiber covering materials, which have checked and cracked due to excessive surface tension, will continue to shrink and open new cracks in the softened film when rejuvenating and refinishing. The solution is to re-cover.

Sound surfaces which were covered with Poly-Fiber and finished with pigmented butyrate dope may be sanded and refinished as instructed in 1 through 6 above, with the exception of using Stits Poly-Fiber Rejuvenator RJ-1200 instead of butyrate rejuvenator.

Poor adhesion of Poly-Dope coatings—or any coating—on old butyrate finishes is caused by unclean surfaces. Thorough cleaning and sanding is necessary. A common cause for poor adhesion for any coating on aluminum pigmented nitrate or butyrate dope is an excessive amount of aluminum pigment added to the clear dope when mixing. If the aluminum pigment can be easily transferred to the finger when rubbing the surface, the proportion of aluminum pigment to dope is too great, and the surface should be sanded to remove the excess aluminum pigmented film before proceeding to finish, or the new finish coats will continue to peel off with masking tape.

Refinishing Nitrate and Butyrate Dope on Cotton or Linen Fabric

Follow all testing, cleaning, sanding and refinishing operations outlined for Dacron/dope surfaces. However, butyrate dope and cotton or linen finishing tape should be used on all repairs to both nitrate and buytrate coatings on cotton and linen to retain fabric tension. Never use nitrate dope over butyrate dope; it will check after drying several weeks.

Refinishing Epoxy Coated Dacron Fabric

Dacron fabric coated with modified epoxy resins (Eonnex) which has become brittle, cannot be completely rejuvenated to the same degree as conventional dope or Poly-Tone coatings. However, refinishing as suggested here will have considerable influence in relieving the brittleness.

Due to the cost, it is not practical to strip the epoxy resin off the fabric. If large, open cracks are present, and exposure damage has already occurred to the fabric through the cracks, complete re-covering may be the most practical.

If the fabric tests satisfactory and the coating is exclusively epoxy resin, follow steps 1 through 6 above, except use RJ-1200 Rejuvenator instead of butyrate rejuvenator. If the surface has been refinished with synthetic enamel, strip the enamel off with Stits Paint Stripper, and follow steps 3 through 6, using RJ-1200 Rejuvenator.

Note: An improved Eonnex Process was announced in April, 1978, after the above was written. See Chapter 8.

Refinishing Synthetic Enamel Surfaces

Synthetic enamel finishes cannot be rejuvenated. Therefore, if the underlying dope film on the fabric is to be rejuvenated, the enamel must be removed first. A decision must be made as to whether the remaining service life of the fabric warrants the extra work of stripping, rejuvenating, and refinishing. It is not economically feasible to strip large areas.

If stripping is decided upon, work small areas with Stits Paint Stripper or an equivalent brand. As soon as the enamel surface has wrinkled and softened, wash off and neutralize with water to avoid penetrating the underlying dope film. Thoroughly clean and sand the underlying Poly-Dope, nitrate, or butyate dope surface, and refinish as outlined in steps 3 through 6 above. Use Stits Poly-Dope Rejuvenator RJ-1200 if the underlying coating is a Stits product.

Do not use commercial paint strippers containing paraffin on fabric. The paraffin may penetrate the fabric weave and prevent adhesion of the new coatings.

If the fabric tests satisfactory, the dope film sound and the enamel finish sound (no cracks), but faded and chalking, it may be refinished with Stits Aero-Thane. A thorough washing and sanding as outlined in steps 1 through 3 is recommended, followed with

Aero-Thane finish before the surface becomes contaminated from handling or weather.

If the fabric is good and the problem is inadequate coating buildup and poor fabric protection, a thorough cleaning, two parts of aluminum pigmented Aero-Thane (AO-220M) Enamel, and Aero-Thane Enamel color finish is recommended.

Some brands of synthetic enamel such as DuPont Dulux can be re-coated with Aero-Thane after aging only 36 hours; and other brands, such as Ditzler, will show slight indications of wrinkling after aging as long as 20 days. Based on various tests, it is Stits's assumption that most synthetic enamels can be refinished successfully with Aero-Thane after they have aged over a year. However, Stits recommends testing a small area beforehand.

Since Poly-Tone contains Ketone solvents which usually swell and lift enamel in a few areas, it is not recommended as a refinishing agent over enamel.

Refinishing Nitrate or Butyrate Dope on Fiberglas Fabric

Follow the testing, cleaning, and rejuvenation procedures outlined in 1 through 6 above. Any repairs should be made with butyrate dope using Fiberglas cloth and finishing tapes of a quality equal to the original material. See Chapter 7.

Chapter 6

The Ceconite Process

The following procedures are taken from Ceconite's Procedure Manual 101, and Ceconite's Technical Bulletins FAB-101 and FIN-101. These instructions are simple, and may be easily followed by any A&P mechanic or individual having previous fabric experience. In the absence of specific directions, the techniques, procedures, and standards of FAA Advisory Circular 43.13 will govern.

Airframe Covering

When the old cover is removed, write down and sketch the method employed to attach the fabric to the airframe. Save the old cover for use as a pattern for locating openings, grommets, inspection rings, determining rib cord lacing areas and spacing, etc.

Before removing the old fabric, however, the careful craftsman will accurately weigh and determine the Center of Gravity (CG) of each control surface. Record this data and retain for possible FAA inspection reference. After re-covering and refinishing, reweigh and determine the CG. This step is important on high speed airplanes to prevent possible flutter.

Normally, this should not be a problem, because Ceconite 101 fabric and the standard Ceconite finishes weigh exactly the same as Grade A cotton and the usual dope finishes. But in cases where other than a standard finish is planned, extra precautions should be taken to preserve control surface balance.

Following proper airframe preparation, Ceconite fabric may be installed by either the envelope or blanket method, or by the cemented method.

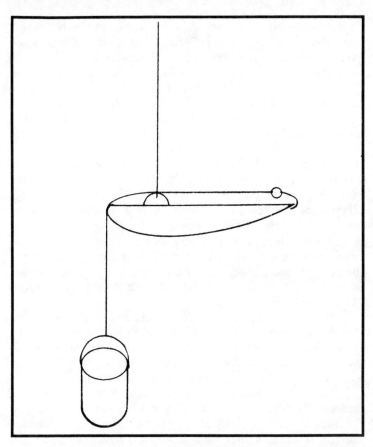

An easy method of recording CG data is suggested by Ceconite. Suspend the covered control surface by its hinges and attach an empty water pail. Add water until the surfaces balances in level position. Weigh the pail of water and record. After the surface is re-covered and refinished, repeat the above procedure. If the weight of the final pail is the same or less than that of the original, the surface is acceptable. If the weight of the final pail exceeds that of the original, the surface must be re-balanced in accordance with manufacturer's instructions.

Envelopes or blankets must be installed in the identical manner of the manufacturer's original envelope, with particular attention to attach method, rib cord lacing areas and spacing (or screws or clips). Machine-sewn seams, baseball hand-stitching, lock knots, seine knots, seam directions, and over-lap areas must duplicate the manufacturer's original covering or adhere to FAA Advisory Circular 43.13 when deviating from the original covering. Either Ceconite Super Seam Cement or a comparable aviation cement will be used in areas calling for cemented joints. Dope may be used for laying surface (finishing) tapes, etc.

On some low-speed aircraft which do not exceed the "never-exceed speed" given in 43.13, Ceconite 101 fabric may be attached to the longerons with Ceconite Super Seam Cement.

The cemented method of covering using Ceconite Super Seam Cement is not restricted to aircraft with "never-exceed speeds" of 150 mph or under, and therefore may be used on any fabric-covered airplane (or glider) and/or fabric-covered control surfaces. The cemented method of covering is recommended on all aircraft where fabric width is sufficient to cover an entire side of a surface. If this is not possible, the fabric may be sewn in panels as described in the blanket method. In the cemented method of covering wings, the fabric may be run spanwise on one side and cemented with Super Seam to the leading and trailing edges as well as to the root ribs and wingtips. The opposite side is then applied using Super Seam with at least a 4-inch over-lap at the leading edge, a 3-inch over-lap at the trailing edge, and at least a 1-inch over-lap at the tips. Surface tape of 6-inch width should be cemented over the leading edge over-lap, and at least 3-inch width tape cemented over the trailing edge and wingtip over-laps.

On the fuselage, fabric should be applied on opposite sides with Super Seam Cement, then applied using the cement with at least a 1-inch over-lap over the longerons and fabric previously applied to the adjacent sides. Surface tape at least 2-inches in width is then cemented over the over-lap seams using Super Seam.

For the best results, one should of course use Ceconite tapes and threads developed for the Ceconite Process. These include Ceconite D-693 or D-415 Rib Lacing Cord; Ceconite D-69 Machine Sewing Thread and D-207 Hand Sewing Thread, along with the Ceconite Surface (finishing) Tapes, and pressure-sensitive Ceconite Reinforcing Tapes.

It is essential that Ceconite rib lacing and sewing threads be used with the Ceconite Process. Surface tapes may be either pre-doped cotton (TSO C-15), Ceconite, or Air Fibre. Reinforcing tapes may be either Special Ceconite Process or cotton. However, if cotton tapes are used it should be understood that a comparable fabric-to-tape life expectancy cannot be expected.

The Tautening Process

Whatever the method employed in attaching Ceconite to the airframe, this fabric should be installed on the structure slightly looser than when covering with cotton fabric. Don't be concerned about fabric wrinkles as these will vanish upon application of heat. Ceconite is given an initial shrinking to first remove the wrinkles and general slackness. Final tautening is then accomplished, followed by

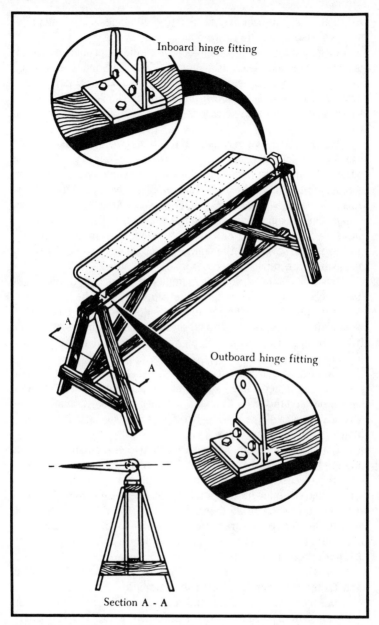

Inboard hinge fitting

Outboard hinge fitting

A

A

Section A - A

Shop-type balancing jig for control surfaces.

rib lacing. The covering is then ready for installation of the surface tapes, inspection rings, reinforcement and grommets, according to the Ceconite Manual 101. *However*, Ceconite Technical Bulletin

FIN-101 makes it plain that rib-stitching and tapes *follow* the prime and two base coats of nitrate dope.

In general, Ceconite shrinkage is in direct proportion to the degree of applied heat; 400 degrees F will shrink unrestricted Ceconite approximately 10%, or five inches in a 50-inch width. Coverings for gliders and light-framed aircraft should initially provide approximately one-inch slack per 50 inches to preclude structural warpage.

Ceconite 101, when subjected to 240 degrees F (household flat iron on "Wool" setting), shrinks to a satisfactory degree of tautness—such as produced by approximately five coats of dope on cotton fabric. *Discontinue the heat process when the envelope has acquired the approximate desired degree of tautness. Do not over-tauten.* On a strong airframe component such as the structure of a DC-3, B-25, etc., an increase in heat will not cause airframe distortion. However, with light airframes, such as sailplanes, Aeroncas and Cubs, care must be taken not to over-tauten.

Since Ceconite fabric shrinks immediately, only two seconds of heat application is required. Longer application of heat does not generally produce further shrinkage. Furthermore, damage to wooden members, other fabrics, and electrical wiring could result from prolonged (10 seconds) application of heat above 240 degrees F.

On shrinking large surfaces (i.e., fuselage and wings), best results are obtained using two or three applications of heat, removing the slack on the first pass, with the main tautening coming on the second coverage. This is similar to spray painting, using two coats rather than a single massive coat.

For initial shrinkage, it is desirable to use a two-man team, each equipped with an iron set on "Wool," and working on opposite sides.

In rare cases where satisfactory tautness is not produced by this degree of heat, the temperature may be raised. Raise the iron temp in increments of 25 degrees, up to a 400-degree maximum, until the desired results are obtained. No amount of direct sunlight in hot weather will further tauten the fabric once it has been "heat set" at 240 degrees F or more.

For the tautening process, a hand-held source of controlled heat is required, and the electric iron method is the best. A household steam iron is an excellent and safe source of controlled heat for removing general slackness. An electric iron set on "Wool" temperature should be used in direct contact with Ceconite for final tautening. Due to the low heat output, electric heat lamps of less than 500 watt ratings are generally slow and unsatisfactory.

Whatever the heat source employed, best results are obtained by keeping the heat source in motion at a rate of approximately five inches per second. A motion akin to every day household ironing is most satisfactory. First, side-to-side, then covering the same area in a top-to-bottom ironing motion to insure uniform shrinkage of all areas.

Care must be taken not to heat Ceconite fabric in excess of 450 degrees F as the fabric will melt and its strength seriously deteriorate. If through error Ceconite is heated above this temperature, the destroyed area will lose its cloth weave and assume a celluloid-like appearance.

Small areas of doped Ceconite may be further tautened with heat by *cautiously* applying an electric iron in direct contact at a lightly increased temperature setting. However, prolonged application of heat (10 seconds or more) at temperatures of 300 degrees F or more may cause discoloration of the dope. Again, caution must be stressed, and this step should be eliminated if possible.

Non-shrinking nitrate and butyrate dopes will generally not produce further measurable tautness. However, regular butyrate dopes will continue to tauten over a period of months, and on light-framed airplanes the envelope must be somewhat looser to allow for further shrinkage when using regular butyrate. As a rule of thumb, maximum tautening is achieved if a coin will bounce when dropped on the fabric surface. But if regular butyrate dope is used, don't seek maximum tautness.

Ceconite Technical Bulletin FAB-101

C.W. Lasher of Southern Aeronautical Corporation, with a great deal of experience applying the Cecnite Process, is the author of Ceconite's Tech Bulletin FAB-101, and since it contains so much practical advice, we reproduce it here verbatim with Ceconite's kind permission:

Before attempting to shrink a cover, take a scrap piece of Ceconite and tack it over a frame or over a board. Tack, staple, or cement all four sides. Use a home-type electric iron with adjustable heat settings. Voltage varies with different locations and different irons are calibrated differently so select the lowest heat setting on your iron that will shrink the fabric. The lowest heat gives you more time to work. Too much heat will make your work too fast and can also burn a hole in the fabric.

Try a setting just below "Wool;" let the iron heat up and run it over the sample as if you were ironing a shirt. If it does not shrink, move the setting up toward "Wool" until you reach the setting where shrinking begins, and use that setting. You can tell if the iron is too hot; it will begin to drag or stick on the fabric before it burns the fabric.

After you shrink the sample and get the feel of it, take the point of your iron and touch the wrinkles, creases, or puckers at the sides and corners and learn how to remove them. You are now ready to go to work, but remember these principles: Ceconite will shrink as long as you leave the iron on it so don't fool around. Pass the iron briskly across the fabric and keep moving. Ceconite cannot be loosened up once it is shrunk, unless you open a seam, so be careful not to over-tauten.

Apply the sheet or slip cover the same degree of slack as you would with Grade A cotton or linen. That is, not baggy, not tight, just snug; but slightly on the loose side. This is not critical with Ceconite as it will draw up perfectly no matter how baggy the fabric is. However, a very loose fit will distort somewhat as it draws up, and will result in the sewn seams being a little wavy instead of being straight. This will not hurt anything, but won't look professional.

Be sure your iron is set on the proper heat setting, and give the entire surface a fast, light pass, top and bottom. Don't try to do all the shrinking on the first pass. Bring the cover up to a point where the looseness is out of it, but still not up to the final tautness. At this point, remove creases and puckers. To avoid applying unnecessary heat on a light-framed airplane, just run lightly *the point* of the iron, or the *edge* of the iron, over the crease or pucker and it will disappear without heating the fabric with the entire flat surface of the iron.

Remember, the fabric shrinks only where the iron touches it. Bend down and sight across the fabric surface to see fine, hair-like creases and remove them as described above. Dope will not appreciably shrink Ceconite, Therefore, all imperfections should be removed before doping if you want to achieve a perfect, professional looking job. Dope does have a slight tautening effect on Ceconite. Therefore, if you are in doubt with regard to how tight is tight, leave the fabric on the loose side or use nontautening dope products.

Ceconite Over Plywood

For covering plywood surfaces, Ceconite 103 is preferred. Specifically, plywood surfaces will be first refinished and sealed. Any irregularities will be filled and smoothed to eliminate trapped moisture condensation. Next, apply four coats of nitrate or butyrate dope to the plywood surface. After the dope dries, attach Ceconite 103 fabric to the plywood surface using Ceconite Super Seam Cement in a one-inch wide strip around the edges. When dry, shrink the fabric with a streaming steam iron, or household iron in direct contact, to a glove-tight fit. Finally, brush on two coats of thinned, clear dope and then complete the finish (see Ceconite Finishing Procedure following).

Agricultural airplane receives extra attention when re-covering aft fuselage due to corrosive influence of the chemicals dispensed.

Ceconite Repairs

With the FAA Advisory Circular 43.13-1A & 2 (Section 3) as a guide, repairs are effected using Ceconite 101 fabric and D-207 Hand Sewing Thread. Ceconite Super Seam Cement or aviation cement is used for the adhesive, and the procedures previously described are utilized. For small patches it is not necessary to remove the finish coat. Merely scuff the surface with No. 320 sandpaper, use Super Seam Cement, and finish in a normal manner. Small patches of Ceconite do not require heat-tautening.

When making repairs it is important to remember that nitrate dope will not adhere to butyrate dope because the nitrate solvents are of a lower order and cannot dissolve butyrate.

Extreme or over-tautness can usually be relieved where Super Seam Cement attach methods are used. Acetone or Methyl Ethyl Keytone (MEK) may be used to soften the cemented laps and relieve over-tight covering. MEK and acetone will quickly evaporate with no impairment to the bond.

Clear lacquer or acrylic enamels combine with and dilute the dope solids which often relieves extreme tautness.

Ceconite Finishing Procedures

Step 1. Three brush coats of nitrate dope with the initial coat thinned about 30% with nitrate thinner, and the other coats thinned to brushing consistency. A quart of

Super Seam Cement added to each gallon, particularly the first coat, improves adhesion.

Step 2. Accomplish rib stitching; lay tapes and install grommets (use plenty of dope). Here also a quart of Super Seam Cement per gallon of dope will improve adhesion.

Step 3. For the buildup coats, spray or brush three coats of clear dope and then two coats of aluminum dope, using three to four ounces of aluminum powder per gallon before thinning. Use of more aluminum powder per gallon will probably result in peeling.

Step 4. Very light sanding with No. 320 Wet-R-Dry sandpaper, primarily to remove cotton nap (if cotton surface tapes are used) and any blemishes. Ceconite is a smooth multi-filament and requires little or no sanding. At this time, if the surface is opaque to light you may proceed to the color coats; otherwise, an additional aluminum coat is required.

Step 5. For a good finish, three color coats are generally required. Somewhat better gloss will result if the final color coat has approximately 30% retarder added.

Important Be certain that your material is FAA approved. All Ceconite 101 material is stamped "FAA PMA Ceconite 101" at one-yard intervals along the selvage edge and also have gray or black identification lines running the length of the material.

Notes It is necessary to achieve dope penetration of fabric and thoroughly coat Ceconite fiber on all sides in order to achieve mechanical adhesion in addition to the natural adhesion of dope. Nitrate dope is preferred as having better adhesive qualities than butyrate dope, and is preferred for Step 1. Butyrate is used after Step 1.

While many prefer enamel for the color coats this procedure is not always advisable on Ceconite because of poor enamel-to-dope bond, and the fact that a rejuvenation or major repair requires removal of the enamel. Furthermore, when enamel is applied over non-tautening butyrate dope the plasticizers may migrate, preventing cure of the enamel. If an enamel finish is mandatory, be sure to thoroughly sand the doped surface to provide for a mechanical bond. Also avoid the use of non-tautening dopes if enamel is to be used. For Arctic service, the all-dope finish is by far the best.

For gliders and sailplanes using Ceconite 103, experience has shown that all coats can be sprayed rather than brushing the initial coats since brushing tends to drop through. Also, the number of clear coats may be reduced by 50%.

Ceconite Technical Bulletin FIN-101

The following Ceconite Technical Bulletin elaborates on the Ceconite finishing process, though these procedures remain essentially the same, except for elimination of the sanding requirement, as those used in finishing Grate A cotton or linen:

Prime Coat

Apply the first coat of dope using a semi-rigid bristle brush. Make sure there is a thorough dope penetration of the fabric. Nitrate dope, depending on its initial consistency, is thinned 30% to 50% with nitrate thinner. For adhesion assurance, a quart of Super Seam Cement added to each gallon of nitrate dope is recommended on the prime coat.

Prime coat dope should be of a good brushing consistency, and should not be of a viscosity that allows it to flow through the fabric on the reverse fabric's interior, thus causing spots. Before application of the following base coat make sure the prime coat is thoroughly dry. Normal drying time will range between 30 minutes to one hour. Again, we stress the importance of working the prime coat into the fabric to insure adhesion.

Base Coats

Apply two base coats over the prime coat, using nitrate dope of the same consistency as that of the prime coat. The base coat should be brushed on the fabric. If good penetration is achieved with the prime coat, base coats do not have to be worked into the fabric. The second base coat, along with all consecutive dope coats, should be brushed on rather than worked in. Here again, it is important to allow each previous coat of dope to dry thoroughly before any additional dope application.

Rib Stitching/Finishing Tapes

Accomplish necessary rib stitching and apply tapes and grommets. Tapes should be applied with nitrate dope over the nitrate base coat. To insure surface tapes that lay down and stay in place, pre-doped Ceconite Surface Tapes are recommended, and the use of one quart of Super Seam Cement to each gallon of nitrate dope is suggested. Rib lacing cord D-693 (Ceconite) is a necessity.

Buildup Coats

Apply three to four coats of clear butyrate dope. The buildup coats can be either sprayed or brushed. If brushing is desirable, an easy brushing consistency is recommended, and brush coats should be alternated at right angles to insure uniformity. In general, more coats of thinner dope provide a more durable finish than fewer coats of a heavy or unthinned dope.

Optional Sanding

Since Ceconite has no nap as does cotton, it requires no sanding. However, if cotton surface tapes are used, or for some reason unwanted particles of dust, etc., appear in the buildup coat, you may wish to sand lightly with No. 320 Wet-R-Dry sandpaper. It is important to make sure that the surface is completely free of sanding residue before proceeding.

A method to insure uniform sanding to the entire aircraft is to apply one coat of aluminum dope and remove entirely with No. 240 sandpaper. Under normal conditions this is certainly optional, and should be employed moderately if not eliminated.

Aluminum Coats

Apply two to three spray or brush coats of aluminum dope over the butyrate buildup coats. The application of the aluminum dope coats will make the surface opaque to light. It will also give more depth to the color coats. The proper formulation for aluminum dope is 3 to 4 oz (maximum) of aluminum powder per gallon of butyrate dope thinned to a proper brushing or spraying consistency.

Color Coats

Three color coats are generally required. Gloss can be enhanced by adding 30% butyrate retarder to the last pigmented color coat.

Enamel has been used on Ceconite with a great deal of success. If enamel, rather than pigmented butyrate finish is desired, normal methods of priming and painting should be followed. However, it must be noted that there is no way of removing a painted finish without damaging the underlying dope film and possibly the fabric. An enameled finish can't be rejuvenated and is difficult to repair.

It should be noted that slight variations to the above have been instituted satifactorily. There is apparently a degree of latitude which can be used in applying dope to Ceconite (or to any other fabric for that matter). The above procedure was derived from a great deal of research and practical experience. We at Ceconite can insure the most satisfactory fabric and finish available to the aircraft owner if the above recommendations are followed.

CECONITE, INC.
4677 Worth Street,
Los Angeles, CA 90063

Chapter 7
The Razorback Method

The Razorback Method of Aircraft Covering is considered to meet the requirements of FAA Advisory Circular 20.44 for external covering of aircraft structures. Under a letter of authority issued to Razorback Fabrics, Inc., dated September 29, 1965, from the FAA, aircraft re-covered with the Razorback Method may be released to service by authorized persons (FAR 43.7) in the normal manner.

It is no longer necessary for a conformity inspection to be conducted on installations of Razorback on new aircraft types.

When a complete aircraft has been covered with the Razorback Method, a Razorback decal must be installed on both sides of the vertical fin or rudder before the craft can be returned to service. It is also required that such decals be installed on each component part of aircraft covered by Razorback Fiberglas which does not consitute a complete aircraft; such requirements applying to certified aircraft.

When the aforementioned have been completed, return aircraft to service by FAA Form 337, referencing installation instructions No. 39-8, dated June 1, 1977 (which are reproduced here).

All Razorback Method products are FAA-PMA approved. Reports of evaluation tests, or any additional information desired, may be obtained from: Razorback Fabrics, Inc., P.O. Box 217, Manila, Arkansas 72442.

Precautionary Measures

A small test sample of Razorback Fiberglas cloth should be completed before attempting to cover the aircraft components.

Razorback cloth is shipped on paper tubes to prevent creasing, and should remain on the tubes until actual use.

Several precautionary measures should be taken before attempting Razorback covering. All contact surfaces should be free of sharp edges. Wooden cap strips should be sanded lightly to remove the sharp edges of dope-proof paint or varnish. All lap seams of leading and trailing edge metal should be taped with industrial tape. The above measures are necessary to prevent the Razorback cloth from snagging on installation.

Treatment of Wood and Metal Surfaces

All wood surfaces, such as catwalks, wood-covered panels, etc., should be treated with two coats of butyrate dope. Allow sufficient time for drying before proceeding. On metal surfaces, especially on agricultural aircraft, we highly recommend that tubing, stringers, and all metal fittings be treated with an epoxy primer. The high rate of rust and corrosion found in agricultural aircraft can be greatly reduced or eliminated entirely by using a good grade of rust and corrosion inhibitor.

The Razorback Method

Use only a high grade, name brand cellulose acetate butyrate dope. Other dopes will not work chemically with Razorback cloth. This cloth comes to you especially pre-treated to ease installation. The pre-treating of Razorback cloth is a highly controlled process, developed after much research, and should not be tampered with. It is compatible only with CAB dope.

The blanket method of covering is employed. With the wide range in widths of material available (from 44 to 72 inches), any aircraft can be covered with Razorback Aircraft Covering.

Information on high quality dopes, thinners, and other accessories is available from Razorback on request. This company has all such materials ready for immediate shipment.

Covering Wing Panels

Install 72-inch glass cloth lengthwise from the butt to the tip on the bottom side of the panel. Align the cloth at least one inch past the trailing edge and clamp the cloth in place with two or three clothes pins.

Stick the cloth down on the trailing edge with cellulose acetate butyrate dope (CAB) or any other approved adhesive and allow to dry. On leading edge metal or large areas where the cloth comes in contact with metal, air pockets and blisters will form. These may be eliminated before they occur by using a squeegee or a cloth folded

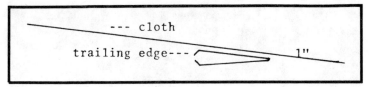

Attachment method for Razorback cloth.

into a pad. Start at the center of the leading edge while holding tension on the cloth, lightly brush a coat of dope on the leading edge metal a square foot at a time.

You may apply the dope on top of the cloth rather than under it. Immediately, use the squeegee or pad, starting at the edge of the leading edge metal, and stroke down and around the leading edge, putting enough tension on the cloth to eliminate wrinkles in the open bay areas.

Caution: Do not pull the cloth too tight. Pull just snug enough to remove any wrinkles. Continue approximately a foot at a time toward the butt, then proceed sticking the tip down, and then the butt. Trim the excess cloth neatly to assure a minimum of a 2-inch doped seam when the top piece of cloth is installed.

Make the strokes while the dope is still wet, and use caution to avoid creasing the cloth with the squeegee.

Turn the wing over and stick down the one-inch trailing edge over-lap. Also stick down the trimmed area along the leading edge, tip, and the butt. Allow to dry. Then lightly sand the edges of the cloth to insure a perfect lap. Roll out the top piece of cloth, cut off at the proper length, and proceed as detailed above. Trim excess material and insure an adequate 2-inch lap.

On certain aircraft, the wing cord is too great to allow covering in the manner just described. The following alternate should be employed, using appropriate width Razorback cloth:

Start at the trailing edge and wrap around the leading edge and back around to the trailing edge. Install the cloth so that a doped seam will occur over a rib. Plan it so that the cloth will extend an inch or so beyond and along the rib. Stick the fabric on the rib temporarily

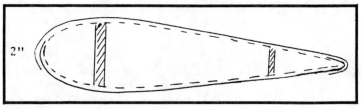

Attachment method for Razorback cloth.

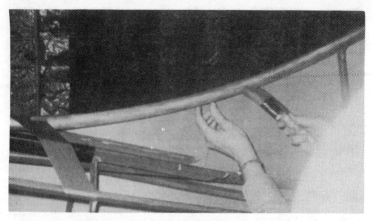

Method of attaching Razorback cloth to vertical fin.

as a means of holding the fabric in place. With the next piece of cloth, extend the selvaged edge of the cloth on the oppoite side of the rib, which will afford an approximate 2-inch doped seam. Dope the fabric on the rib only, to prevent drooping of the cloth parallel to the rib. Subsequent steps in the doping procedure will afford the seam to bond itself properly.

Ailerons

Applicable size Razorback glass cloth is stuck with CAB dope at trailing edge; wrap around the aileron lengthwise back to the trailing

Cloth stops at fin rib, and scrap cloth used form there to top.

edge. Stick again, thereby accomplishing a 2-inch lap. Again, use caution not to pull too tight—just snug, with the wrinkles removed. If Razorback cloth is pulled more than fingertight, the subsequent natural tautening of the material can result in serious warping of an entire component. Cut the surplus material on the outboard and inboard edges and stick in the same manner.

In the case of larger ailerons, such as the DC-3, apply the glass cloth in the same manner as described for wing panels.

Fuselage

The fuselage is normally covered in four sections. One sheet at bottom being attached to corner skin stiffeners or longerons by full-bodied butyrate dope, one sheet on each side, and one sheet on top; all being installed in the same manner. Again, exercise caution not to install under too much tension—just enough to remove the wrinkles and allow a snug fit.

Where sewn seams are called for, lap the material a minimum of 2-inches and dope the seams together. The 2-inch lap-seam has a tensile strength exceeding 100 pounds. Therefore, French felled seams or hand-sewn seams are not required with this material.

Empennage and Center Section

Empennage components are covered in the same manner as the ailerons. On aircraft having center sections, cover in the same way as a wing panel, using 72-inch material.

Installation of top piece of Razerback or fuselage.

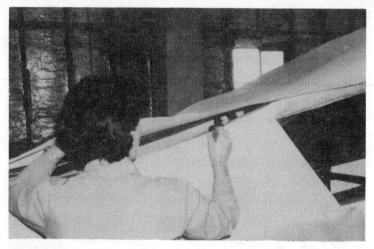

Top piece is trimmed and glude to top longron, over-lapping the side piece.

Doping

Razorback cloth does not require sizing. It is of the utmost importance that the following recommendations be adhered to: *Do not under any circumstances install the first coats of dope by brush or roller.*

> Step 1. Use pressure pot equipment if available; 18 lbs sq/in on pot pressure; 60 lbs sq/in at the gun to insure

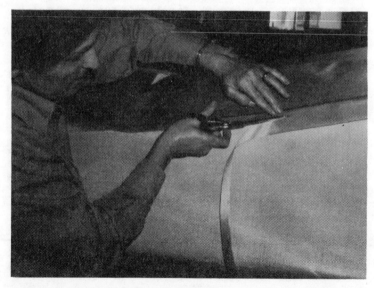

Top piece is trimmed to allow a two-inch over-lap.

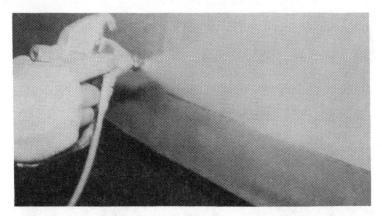

Spraying the first coats of clear cellulose acetate butyrate dope.

proper atomization. A suction type gun may be used but will require a) more thinner, b) more coats, and c) more time between coats for proper curing.

Step 2. Spray the first coat of clear butyrate dope. Thin the dope only to insure proper atomization. *Do not under any circumstances blow or run dope through weave of cloth as this will cause the cloth to orange peel and will not dry taut*. To insure proper adhesion of the dope do not spray too lightly, as the dope will be dry on contact with the surface.

Step 3. The second coat can be sprayed a little heavier than the first, and each succeeding coat a little heavier than the previous one.

Step 4. The first coats will cause Razorback cloth to sag, but subsequent coats will draw it up. The tautening action

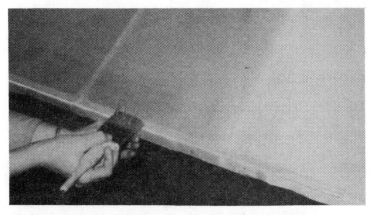

Recovering wing panels; no sewn seams. First, attach trailing edge.

Installation of tapes as detailed in Step #6.

in some cases is a little slower than normal due to humidity or drying conditions. The tautening action will occur between the second and fifth coats, or when the weave has been sealed. Do not apply more than two or three coats of dope in a one-day period to allow sufficient curing and drawing time. If tautening problems occur, do not apply more dope; instead place the surface in the sun and allow to cure before proceeding.

Step 5.   When the weave is completely sealed, and the fabric has tautened, install Razorback reinforcing tapes. At this point, rib stitch cord or other fasteners are applied as in the original manner.

Step 6.   When the surfaces are completely sealed, taut, and free of all wrinkles, install the finishing tapes as follows: All dope lap seams, or where the fabric comes in contact with tubing, trailing edge, etc., should be sanded to eliminate any irregularities. Lap seams will not show through the tape when this is done. You should have someone to assist you on taping installation. Roll out the necessary length and lay along the rib. Dope the fabric over the rib as quickly as possible. The person at the trailing edge picks up the end of the tape and holds the tape on both selvaged edges and places it directly over the rib and holds it tightly. Then the other craftsman holds the other end of the tape at both selvaged edges giving a slight tug to straighten the tape; relaxes slightly, and lays it directly over the rib from his end. The helper at the trailing edge reaches mid-way, and with the palm of his hand rubs over the tape toward the trailing edge with a single stroke. The craftsman at front does the same toward the leading edge. Then roll off enough tape to go around the bottom of the wing; cut it off and let it hang. Move on to the next rib and repeat above. Do not under any circumstances apply dope on top of the tape until the initial coat has thoroughly dried. When all the tapes are installed, then you may go back and brush on a coat of dope on top of the tape and stick down any edges that need it. You may have to slit or snip the selvaged edge to insure that the edges are properly down. Now you build the tapes with sufficient coats of dope to catch up with the cloth. This will require approximately four to five coats, with each coat thoroughly cured, and the tape sanded slightly between the second and third coat or the third and fourth.

Step 7. At this point, you may use non-tautening dope, particularly if your structure will be subject to warping.

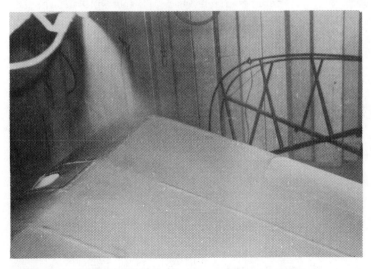

Spraying non-tautening butyrate dope for build-up on Razorback cloth.

Apply two additional coats of non-tautening dope by spraying. Allow to cure. Thereafter, continue to build with two coats of silver-pigmented non-tautening dope. Allow to cure at least overnight and sand thoroughly with 280 grit sandpaper, exercising caution not to sand over rivets, ribs, rib-stitch cord, etc. Most of the silver should be sanded off with the exception of the fills. Be sure to completely remove the sanding residue, and spray one silver pigmented coat as a base coat and to assure protection of the clear butyrate from the sun's ultraviolet rays.

Spray two coats of pigmented dope in the colors of your choice. If an exceptionally slick finish is desired, very light wet-sanding with 320 grit paper may be done, followed by the last finish coat.

Note: Sanding time may be cut more than 50% by the use of an air-driven orbital sander. Exercise caution in sanding over rivets, screw, rib stitching, etc. Although Razorback does not recommend the use of enamel or any polyurethane paints, they can be applied to Razorback. But remember, enamel can not be rejuvenated and is very difficult to patch. Fresh butyrate dope must cure *thoroughly* before any enamel can be applied or peeling is likely.

In a majority of cases, any wrinkles remaining in the finished cover will disappear in a matter of a few days after the aircraft has been exposed to sunlight and fresh air.

The Razorback glass cloth in its original form weighs approximately 3.92 oz per square yard, as opposed to 4 oz for Grade A cotton fabric. Therefore, there will be no appreciable weight change.

Razorback Cloth Over Plywood Surfaces

Step 1. After removing the old fabric, sand all wood surfaces completely clean, removing all of the old varnish, coatings, paints, etc.

Step 2. Apply two coats of clear butyrate dope by brush to the plywood surface. If all of the old varnish has been removed, this dope will dry smooth and slick. If particles of varnish remain you will have a wrinkled surface, similar to applying dope over lacquers or enamel. Once you are positive your surface is clean, apply the two coats of clear butyrate, thinning the first

Thorough sanding of the surfaces.

coat sufficiently for penetration. Allow to cure. Then brush on the second coat and allow to cure. Adhesion can be enhanced by mixing the two coats with one-half Super Seam Cement and one-half dope, with sufficient thinner for brushing.

Step 3. Place the Razorback cloth on the panel, and brush the cloth with a dry, clean brush to remove distortions, air, etc. Hold the fabric in place with masking tape around the edges if necessary.

Step 4. Start in the center of the area with a clean brush and straight butyrate thinner. Use a one-directional stroke working from the center toward the outer edges. This procedure allows the cloth to be imbedded in the underlying dope, and eliminates air blisters. Allow it to cure thoroughly.

Step 5. Brush two coats of clear dope and allow it to cure.

Step 6. Dry-sand with No. 320 grit sandpaper.

Step 7. Brush one coat of clear butyrate dope.

Step 8. Dry-sand, carefully removing all sanding residue.

Step 9. Brush one coat of clear butyrate dope.

Step 10. Dry-sand.

Step 11. After these four brush coats and three sandings, all surfaces should be very glassy; and at this point

109

normal finishing with pigmented butyrate may be completed.

Repair and Patching

Cut out the damaged area, either round or square. Cut the patch of Razorback glass cloth at least two or more inches larger than the area to be patched. Apply clear, full-bodied butyrate dope to the outer two inches of the surface being repaired. Attach the patch with a minimum of two-inch lap in all directions, smoothing out the surface wrinkles by hand. Allow a few minutes to dry. Subsequent coats of dope may be applied in accordance with normal doping procedure. If the surrounding surface is hard and old, use a rejuvenator to soften the lap area. Hand-sewing or baseball stitching are not required, as the lap seams will have a tensile strength in excess of 100 lbs of pull.

Inspection

The butyrate dope on Razorback glass installations must be inspected at the periodic inspections. Visually inspect the dope for cracks or signs of deterioration. If these conditions are found to exist, rejuvenate with CAB dope rejuvenator and refinish with a color wash coat.

No pull or punch test is required or recommended for Razorback cloth. A notation in the airframe log book and FAA Form 337 should state only visual inspection of the butyrate dope required.

Razorback Fiberglas cloth is tough.

Trouble Shooting

Non-tightening of Razorback Cloth (or cotton and linen).

    a. Fabric applied too loosely
    b. Large amount of thinner used
    c. Large amount of retarder used.
    d. Clear dope over plasticized
    e. Excessive first coat

Blushing

    a. Humidity too high for doping
    b. Moisture in spray system
    c. Dope applied over a moist surface

Pin Holing

    a. Water or oil in spray system
    b. Undercoat not thoroughly dry
    c. Too fast surface drying
    d. Coating film too heavy

Bubbles and Bridging

    a. Dope too cold to use
    b. Dope not brushed out
    c. Temperature of dope room too high

Runs and Snags

    a. Too heavy a coat of material

Non-Drying of Dope

    a. Oil, grease, or wax on surface

Bleeding

    a. Organic pigments or dyes in undercoats that are soluble in dope solvents of top coats. Always spray bleeding colors last; or better yet, use only non-bleeding colors

White Spots

    a. Water in the spraying system or spraying over a wet surface

Brown Spots

    a. Oil coming through the spray system

Orange Peel

    a. Spray technique in error
    b. Pressure too high
    c. Fast-drying thinner
    d. Cold, damp draft over surface

Wrinkling

    a. Reaction of dope solvents on primer or enamel type under-
coat

Overspray

    a. Spray technique in error

    b. Fast-drying thinner

    c. Spot spraying certain areas

Fish Eye

    a. Silicon contamination on the work; wax or polish

Chapter 8
The Eonnex Process

Eonnex 7600 instructions have been approved by the FAA and all procedures must be closely followed. Procedures referred to in other publications do not apply to Eonnex covers, except where reference is made here to AC 43.13-1A & 2.

If you have been accustomed to working with dope and fabric you'll find that a few of the methods used in the Eonnex Process are somewhat different than those employed with other products. However, none of the procedures are difficult; in fact, most are easier than other methods and will effect substantial labor savings.

Untrained personnel have made highly successful Eonnex installations with no other instruction than that provided in the Eonnex Manual which we reproduce here with the kind permission of Mr. Bill Lott of Eonair, Inc., 417 Watts Drive, Bakersfield, CA 93307 (Bakersfield Airpark).

Airframe Preparation

Before an Eonnex cover is installed, it should be ascertained that the structure and its components to be covered have adequate corrosion or rot protection, as the life expectancy of Eonnex cover is several times that of doped fabric. Due to the long life expectancy of Eonnex covers, the underlying structure should be prepared with utmost consideration given to protective coatings. Eonite No. 22 Sealer or equivalent is recommended for use on wood, and Eonite No. 19 Paint or equivalent for use on metal. Make sure that all surfaces are clean, dry and free of any loose or brittle paint or varnish. Areas of the structure where it is not desired to have the fabric adhere may be taped with cellophane, masking, or polyethelene tape to reduce adhesion.

1. On some wings, it may be desirable to run two or three additional lines of tying tape between the ribs instead of the usual one. Eonnex No. 3 or 7623 tape may be used for this purpose. The reason for these additional internal tapes is that the fabric pull is not even at all points during the application of the tautening heat and the ribs may tend to distort due to unequal compression loads. After the coating is applied this condition will not exist. These additional tapes should run from rib to rib in a straight line on both the top and bottom of the wing. Only the original tape is tied on the diagonal, that is, from the top of one rib to the bottom of the adjoining rib. Tapes should be tied to the ribs in such a manner that the tape spans are on the inside of the wing and do not contact the fabric except at the points where the tape wraps around the rib cap strip.

2. Blanket or envelope method may be used with Eonnex fabric.

2.1 Cemented laps of three inches minimum width must be made when using the blanket method and 7602 Cement. This applies to all aircraft.

3. Fabric may be cut and installed on the bias if necessary to hold waste to a minimum.

4. *Sewing*: Machine-sewed seams must be accomplished in accordance with accompanying Table 1, or AC 43.13-1A & 2 using Eonnex No. 7 Thread.

Table 1 permits the use of either single or double-stitched seams. Single-stitched seams require more stitches per inch. However, if the machine is capable of this fine stitch, an uncoated seam strength of over 100 lbs will result, and the seam will be practically invisible after it is taped and coated.

The thread tension on the machine will usually have to be adjusted somewhat looser than with cotton thread.

A white dust will accumulate on the sewing machine when using No. 7 Thread. This is a dry lubricant on the thread and is a normal condition.

Sewed seams should be used where necessary if a cemented lap joint of at least the required width cannot be made.

4.1 Hand-sewed seams shall be accomplished using Eonnex No. 7 Thread, double.

5. Apply Eonnex 7605 or 7606 fabric to the structure just slightly looser than a conventional cotton cover. Excessive looseness may cause slackness to develop in cold weather.

Recommended positioning of "tying tapes" on wing ribs for the Eonnex Process.

SINGLE STITCHED	7605	7606
SPACING, STITCH LINE TO FABRIC EDGE.		
SELVAGE EDGE	1/8 INCH	1/4 INCH
CUT EDGE	1/2 INCH	5/8 INCH
STITCHES PER INCH	20	24
DOUBLE STITCHED, FELLED SEAM OR LAP SEAM		
SPACING, STITCH LINE TO FABRIC EDGE.		
SELVAGE EDGE	1/16 INCH	1/16 INCH
CUT EDGE	1/8 INCH	1/4 INCH
STITCHES PER INCH	16	16
SPACING BETWEEN STITCH LINES	1/8 INCH	3/16 INCH
NOTE: ALL VALUES ARE MINIMUM.		

Eonnex Table 1.

Edges that are cemented to the structure must be installed using Eonnex 7602 Cement and 7603 Activator, or Eonnex 204 Cement. The 204 Cement must be used to attach fabric if the three-inch minimum lap width requirement cannot be met. Eonnex 204 Cement will be satisfactory for laps having a minimum width of one inch, providing the fabric is unfilled and free of other cements. Care should be taken in cemented areas to insure the fabric of being as free from wrinkles as possible. Small remaining wrinkles may be removed by applying the heated Eonnex iron to the wrinkles after the cement is dry. This will improve the bond as well as remove the wrinkles.

5.1 If the cemented blanket method of installation is used, the following procedure is recommended: A fuselage is used for example. Install top and bottom fabric pieces and heat tauten. Then install the side pieces. This procedure provides a smooth, taut surface to cement the side pieces. Fabric lap joints must have both adhering surfaces of the cloth coated with 7602 Cement and allowed to dry before joining. Apply 7603 Activator to one surface and join while the activated cement is wet.

It is desirable to apply 7602 Cement to all areas of the structure where attachment is to be made, before starting to install any fabric, except areas where 204 Cement is to be used.

When using cement to attach fabric to the structure, allow at least one hour for solvent evaporation before heat-tautening the fabric. Waiting time may be shortened by using the tautening iron adjusted to medium heat to "set" the joint under pressure, after it is dry to the touch.

5.2 When fabric is to be applied over large areas of underlying structure, such as gas tank covers, wing walks, or plywood, it should be determined whether or not the fabric will be in tight contact with such areas once it has been heat-tautened. If areas exist where the fabric will be just slightly raised from the underlying surface or only contact the surface intermittently, it will be best to cement the fabric to such areas before it is tautened with heat. If this is not done, it will be difficult to sand and finish properly. It will not be necessary to tauten these areas except to remove wrinkles.

6. Eonnex fabric must be tautened by two or more applications of heat. The first application is made by the use of a hand-held radiant

The pre-coated Eonnex fabric is tautened in two stages by use of a special Eonnex iron.

heat source, hot air gun, steam iron, or the electric iron adjusted for use on Eonnex. The heat is adjusted to produce a temperature of 225 to 250 degrees F on the surface of the fabric. It is not necessary to completely heat the entire cover to this temperature. The main purpose is to level the cover to a point where the seams are straight, free it from severe sags and wrinkles, and have it in position for further tautening using the Eonnex iron.

6.1 A hand-held electric radiant heater such as a hot plate or a small space heater can be used for the preliminary tautening. A properly designed electric heater will prove to be slightly faster for preliminary tautening than an electric iron. Caution must be observed so as not to overheat the fabric. If the fabric is overheated, excessive tautness will result, and in extreme cases may melt and form holes or cause the cloth to take on a glazed appearance. Avoid applying excessive heat to cemented joints under tension.

6.2 The Eonnex iron or equivalent is set to a higher heat for the second tautening operation than was used for the previous application. The exact setting will be determined by experience. Most structures will easily accept the maximum heat available from the Eonnex iron. Some of the less rigid structures must be tautened at a lower temperature if distortion of the structure is to be avoided. The entire surface, except cemented joints, must be evenly heated with the iron at the highest temperature setting to be used (not necessarily the highest available). The speed of the ironing action should be such that the fabric is completely heated, but not long enough that the underlying structure is damaged from the heat. No more than three seconds of continuous heat should be concentrated in one spot at a time. Fabric areas that are in contact with the underlying structure will require a longer application of heat than areas that are in suspension. If, after the final tautening, wrinkles still exist, they may be removed using the special Close Quarter Iron set to maximum heat. This iron was designed for use in repair work in small areas or in tight places that cannot be reached with a standard iron. It should not be used over large areas as the volume of heat available is limited and the sole plate temperature may drop. The most satisfactory cover results from using the highest heat application in the final tautening that the structure will accept without distorting. Too low a heat can result in slackness developing in the cover at very low atmospheric temperatures.

The use of the Eonnex fabric-tautening iron or equivalent is specified and required for the final tautening because the thermostat is adjusted in such a manner that the fabric cannot be damaged no matter how high the external control is set. This iron provides economical insurance of a properly tautened cover that will not develop wrinkles. The iron has its internal thermostat adjustment

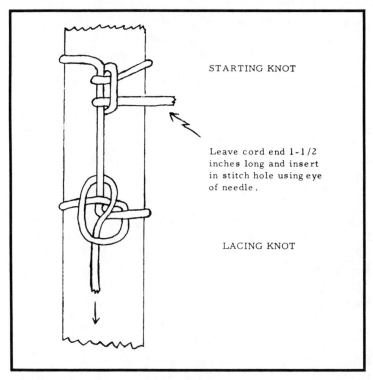

STARTING KNOT

Leave cord end 1-1/2 inches long and insert in stitch hole using eye of needle.

LACING KNOT

Knot system, employing Eonnex No. 9 lacing cord.

set in such a manner that 410 degrees F will not be exceeded when the external temperature control is set to maximum.

The material cost savings on the first cover job will more than pay for the few simple tools required for the proper installation of Eonnex.

The Eonnex coatings will not cause any further shrinking of the cover under any weather conditions.

6.3 Ribs that are slightly bowed after the fabric has been tautened can frequently be straightened by the following procedure: Insert the eye end of a rib-stitching needle through the weave of the fabric and push on the bowed side of the rib until it is straight. While holding it in this position, staples may be driven through the fabric and into the center of the cap strip with an office paper-type stapler. These staples are very fine and will not damage the cap strips. They have adequate strength and will work on light metal as well as wood. The staples need not be removed as they are covered when the reinforcing tapes are installed.

7. *Reinforcing Tapes*: Apply reinforcing tapes Eonnex #3 or 7623 over cap strips or ribs as required. Reinforcing tapes should be

the same width as the cap strips or ribs if rib stitching is used. For other attachment methods the tapes should be ¼-inch minimum. The tapes are supplied with a pressure-sensitive adhesive coating and are installed without the use of cements. They may be removed and respositioned if necessary, without destroying the adhesive.

8. *Cover Attachments*: Install cover attachments. Rib stitch cord Eonnex Part No. 9, rivet, or sheet metal screw attachment spacing must be the same as original, according to 43.13, or two inches on centers. Other methods such as wire clips or springs must be the same as original. See accompanying drawing for the knot system to be used. Rib stitches made with Eonnex No. 9 Cord, rivets, or sheet metal screws into metal ribs do not need to be spaced less than two inches on centers of any aircraft. After a little practice, it will be noted that the Eonnex lacing knot shown is much faster than the conventional knot recommended in 43.13-1A & 2. The best finished appearance will be obtained if the knots and cord are tied to lay alongside the edge of the reinforcing tape and in contact with the underlying fabric, instead of on top of the tape as illustrated.

9. *Surface Tapes & Reinforcements*: Install surface tapes, Eonnex No. 4, 7604, or 7624 over attachments and single-stitched seams. Install reinforcement patches at points where inspection openings are to be cut. Patches should extend one inch around the opening. The reinforcement patches may be cut from Eonnex No. 5A Fiberglas, Eonnex 7605 or 7606 fabric, or 7608. Tapes and reinforcements are applied using Eonnex 7602 and 7603 as in 5.1 above. No. 7608 requires only 7603 Activator.

After the tapes and other reinforcements have been installed, one coat of 7603 Activator should be applied over them. Eonnex 7608 or 7624 Tapes are recommended for installation on curves such as wingtip bows. Tapes 7608 and 7624 can be shrunk with heat to conform with the surface. Eonnex 7604 Tapes are recommended for straight line taping such as over ribs and leading and trailing edges.

9.1 Surface tapes need only be installed over rib stitches or other attachments and over sewed seams. It is not necessary to apply surface tapes completely around the wing or leading or trailing edges unless a seam exists at that point. Tapes are not required over seams that are cemented to the structure for at least one inch on each side. However, they may be desirable from the appearance standpoint.

Surface tapes may be cut with a pointed end rather than straight across. This will prevent any tendency to unravel and presents a better finished appearance. Tapes over cap strips should extend one inch over the solid supporting structure of wing leading edges.

Although not required, it is desirable to apply a surface tape as reinforcement over the stringers and other stress points. Care should be taken when installing surface tapes to be sure that they lay flat and are free from bubbles. Do not attempt to stretch Fiberglas tapes.

Conventional inspection rings are not recommended because they tend to embrittle and fall off with age. A doubler patch of Eonnex fabric or Eonnex 5A glass cloth, with a ring width of one inch, is recommended. If the additional thickness provided by an inspection ring is desired, the ring may be placed between the cover fabric and the doubler, thereby anchoring it permanently in place. Adhesives 7602 and 7603 may be applied with a brush.

10. *Filler Coating, 7601 Black*: Using Eonnex coating applicator pads or spray paint equipment, apply the coating to all of the fabric.

10.1 *Pad Application*: Pour the amount of coating that will be used into a container slightly larger than the applicator pad. Dip the pad into the coating until completely saturated. Holding the pad flat against the fabric, apply one full, wet, even coat. One side of a typical wing can be coated by this method in about 20 minutes.

The Eonnex filler coat is applied with a pad. This operation requires about 20 minutes for an average wing panel.

After the coating has dried, a second full, wet coat is applied. This should be applied by wiping the pad across the surface at a right angle to the direction used in the first application. Drying time for each coat will range from 10 minutes to one hour, depending on temperature, air flow, and humidity.

10.2 *Spray Application*: Coating may be applied in one full, wet coat or two thin coats. The first coat spanwise on a wing, and the second chordwise. The two-coat system will result in less tendency for the coating to run or sag.

11. *Sanding*: After the filler coat has hardened sufficiently (15 minutes to one hour, depending on drying conditions), it is sanded. Just enough sanding should be done to remove any lumps or severe uneveness due to rough tape edges or dirt that may have settled onto the wet coating. This operation should require no more than 10 minutes to sand one side of the average wing. If the surface is smooth and free of foreign matter, this operation may be omitted. Excessive sanding will reduce the coating thickness. Dry sanding is recommended. The best results are obtained using a 150-C No-Fil Durite paper or equivalent. Do not rub in one spot for a long period of time as the friction will heat the coating and cause it to load the paper.

If desired, the coating may now be sanded with either a wet or a dry abrasive up to and including a 400 grit. Following this sanding, the surface should be thoroughly washed with water and allowed to dry. No aromatic or keytone-type solvents should be used to clean the filler coating as they will soften or disolve it.

Most shops have found that a high speed orbital type sander is a good investment because of the sanding-time savings and the very smooth finish obtained.

11.1 If, by accident, the coating is sanded through to a point where the nap of the fabric starts to raise, filler coating may be re-applied to these areas and sanded.

12. A finish paint is applied as desired, and is required to prevent erosion of the filler. Primer coats are usually not needed, and they are not recommended as they are generally quite brittle. Eonnex 7630 Series Polyurethane Paints are recommended. They provide good protection from the environment and are quite flexible at sub-zero temperatures. They have been formulated to be compatible with the other Eonnex coatings.

Care should be used in selecting the finish paint to assure flexibility. Many lacquers, enamels, and acrylic finishes have been found to be too hard and brittle and will ringworm under impact such as hailstones or rough handling in cold weather. Most of the chemical-resistant paints used for agricultural aircraft show excellent adhesion to Eonnex covers. Care should be taken not to apply these paints to an excessive thickness as they are usually more brittle than conventional enamels. There is a difference in the flexibility between various brands of these paints.

Pigmented butyrate dope also provides a satisfactory finish for agricultural aircraft. The chemicals used do not lift dope as they do regular enamels, and the dope is more flexible than many of the chemical-resistant paints.

13. See "Helpful Hints" section following for further information on paints.

14. Inspection openings are cut out and covers installed.

15. Drain holes should be made in the cover as required. Minimum diameter, 3/16 inch; maximum diameter, ¼ inch.

15.1 Drain holes can be made by drilling holes though the surface tapes close to the ribs, or by melting holes through the cover with a hot rod (500 degrees) of the appropriate diameter. A light duty soldering iron with a 3/16-inch tip is ideal for this purpose. The hot iron may be used to seal the edges around other openings.

16. *Weight and Balance*: Eonnex is the lightest weight cover available. Under no circumstances, if it is installed in conformity with the instuctions contained herein, will the weight be greater than the approved cover removed from the aircraft. Rebalance of the control surfaces is not required if they were within tolerance with the old cover and balance weights are not moved or changed. Exception: If more than six coats of dope are used on the cover it may be necessary to check balance. In general, the weight of an Eonnex cover will be from 25% to 60% less than a doped fabric cover.

16.1 If there is a substantial amount of covering done on an aircraft it will probably be advantageous to re-weigh the components covered to gain the benefit of increased useful load. This can amount to eight to 15 pounds on a single wing panel. Weigh the component before the old fabric is removed, then weigh it again after the Eonnex cover is completely finished. Subtract the difference from the empty weight of the aircraft.

17. *Repairs*: If the finish paint on the damaged area is one that will be lifted by cements or coatings in making the repair, the paint should be removed by sanding or the use of suitable paint removers. Eonnex coatings will not be affected by cements, and it will not be necessary to remove them. The surface should be lightly sanded to remove all surface dirt and wax.

When paint strippers are used to chemically remove the finish paint in preparation for repairs or refinishing the aircraft, it should be ascertained that the type of remover will not attack the Eonnex coatings. This may be done by testing the stripper on a small area.

17.1 Cuts or tears may be sewn as outlined in 43.13-1A and 2 using Eonnex Thread No. 7, double. If any wrinkles exist, it may be possible to remove them by application of heat using the special Close Quarter iron. Heat should be applied only enough to remove the wrinkles. If the coating is damaged by the application of the heat, it should be removed by sanding. Surface tape is applied over the sewed area and should extend one inch minimum beyond the edge of the cut or tear.

17.2 Holes may be repaired using Eonnex 7608 or 7605 or 7606 fabric and coatings. All patches must be installed with a cemented edge lap of three inches minimum.

17.3 Cut Eonnex fabric patches of approrpriate size and using 7602 and 7603 Cement on the edges, apply the patch. 7608 requires only 7603 Activator. After the cement has dried, tauten the patch with heat as outlined in instruction 6. The lapped edges should be ironed first to be sure the cement is set. Eonnex coatings, surface tapes if desired, and finish paint are applied in the standard manner to complete the repair.

17.4 *Repairs, General*: Eonnex 7608 Patches are the fastest repairs to make. It is possible to make an airworthy patch repair in less than 10 minutes if force-drying is used. The pitch may be painted at a later time as desired.

17.5 *Dope and conventional fabric* may be used to make repairs following the procedures outlined in 43.13-1A and 2, and instruction 12 above. However, repairs employing these materials will have a considerably shorter life expectancy.

17.6 Coatings, tapes, attachments or other reinforcements to be replaced on Eonnex covers installed as per pre-1976 editions of Eonnex Manual 200 may be installed in conformance with instructions herein beginning with No. 8.

18. *Cover Strength Tests*: Determination of the continued airworthiness of Eonnex coverings can be approximated by the use of a Seybooth or Maule Fabric Tester with the air temperature above 60 degrees F. The most accurate method is a "pull test" on a one-inch strip of the cover, or a one-half inch wide strip with the resulting failing load in pounds multiplied by two. It is not necessary to remove the fabric coatings when conducting these tests, except that dope must be removed when it has been applied as a filler and finish coating. The lower limits specified in 43.13-1A & 2 will govern the acceptable deterioration (normally, 56 lbs tensile).

19. *Material Alternatives*: No material substitutions are permitted except pigmented finish paints.

20. *Covering of Plywood Surfaces*: Plywood surfaces are more difficult to fabric cover and obtain a smooth surface than conventional fabric covered welded tubular or spar and rib structures. This is true regardless of the type of fabric or coatings used. More coatings are

required because both sides of the fabric must be completely filled in order to obtain a smooth finish as well as a good bond to the plywood.

20.1 Surfaces that have been previously covered must have all old fabric and coatings removed to expose the clean, bare wood. Paint stripper may be used for this purpose. All residue left by the paint stripper is removed by using rags saturated in a suitable solvent. The wood should be sanded to remove any possible coating or paint stripper residue.

20.2 On new wood, or wood prepared as described above, the following procedures must be followed: Fill any open joints, cracks, or depressions with suitable filler to insure a smooth surface. Apply a coat of Eonnex 7630 Series Polyurethane Paint to the wood using an Eonnex applicator pad. Allow this coating to dry for at least 16 hours. The coating is then sanded enough to remove any pad marks or foreign matter that may have settled on the surface.

20.3 Apply a coat of Eonnex 7602 Cement to the surface using the applicator pad, and allow to dry. This step may be omitted if Eonnex 7608 fabric is used.

20.4 Eonnex 7605, 7606, 7608, or 5A fabric is cut to fit the surface. The fabric may be applied either diagonal, chordwise, or spanwise. For the smoothest surface, butt joints are made rather than lap joints. To apply, lay the fabric in place on the surface. Place a weight such as a board on the fabric to hold it in position. Fold the fabric back over the weight and apply a coat of 7603 Activator to about 18 inches of the surface. Immediately smooth the fabric on to that part of the surface just coated using a lintfree rag to wipe the fabric smoothly into the wet cement. Fold the fabric back to the point where the activator ends, and apply activator to another 18-inch portion of plywood, and again wipe the fabric smoothly into the surface. The fabric should be completely bonded to the surface. Allow this coating to set for four or more hours and then go over it with the Eonnex tautening iron set about halfway between the "High" and "Low" heat settings to remove any wrinkles or bubbles that may be in the fabric.

20.5 Eonnex surface tapes are applied over the butt joints in the fabric as per instruction 9.

20.6 Apply a coat of 7601 Filler.

20.7 Sand the filler coat, and then finish paint as desired.

Note: The finished weight will be about the same as doped fabric installed over plywood.

21. *Eonnex Manual 200, May, 1963 Edition & Earlier:* Covering installations made per Manual 200 may be repaired per Eonnex 7600, instruction 17.

As with the other synthetic covering processes, the Eonnex Process has been installed on most kinds of fabric-covered air-craft and added to the FAA's approved lists. Aircraft already on the approved lists may be returned to service, after Eonnex installation, by any aircraft mechanic with an Inspector's Rating after filling FAA Form 337 and making the appropriate entry in the airframe logbook. If the craft being covered is a rare bird and none of that make have previously been covered and finished in the Eonnex Process, an FAA Inspector will have to check the work to determine that Eonnex procedures were followed and complete FAA Form 8100-1. The conformity inspection, if required, should be done as soon as the covering has been done except for the painting.

Helpful Hints

Finish Painting: After the 7601 filler coat has been applied and sanded as recommended, the following finish systems have been found satisfactory.

A. Eonnex 7630 Series pigmented urethane enamels. One fog coat; let dry 15 to 30 minutes. Then follow with a full, wet coat.

B. Two cross coats of pigmented butyrate dope.

C. One cross coat of pigmented butyrate; let dry two hours minimum. One fog coat of 7630 clear urethane enamel, followed in 15 to 30 minutes with a full, wet coat.

D. One coat of Eonnex 7640 pigmented emulsion. Let dry. One fog coat of 7630 clear urethane enamel, followed in 15 to 30 minutes with a full, wet coat.

Eonnex urethane enamel is an extremely flexible, high-gloss material. As a top coat for the Eonnex cover it provides a crack and abrasion resistance even after long aging, superior to anything tested by Eonnex. It may be used over properly primed metal. This enamel is a two-part mix, and the thinners used are flammable. Adequate ventilation should be provided.

Eonnex 7640 pigmented emulsion paint is available in a wide range of colors. It is applied over Eonnex 7601 filler and properly primed metal. Only one thin coat is required, enough to provide the desired color. This coating is not formulated to give a long term service life unless it is protected by a clear over-coat which provides the gloss and wear surface. Eonnex 7640 emulsion paint offers advantages not available with any other FAA-approved aircraft covering system. Multi-color paint jobs may be accomplished in a minimum of elapsed time. Dry time is very fast—five minutes to one hour—depending on ambient temperature and humidity. Masking for other colors may be done as soon as the paint is dry. Sags or overspray can be washed off immediately with a wet cloth. This paint is thinned with water, but is not water soluble once it has dried.

Craftsmanship is 95% of a first class aircraft re-cover job, whatever the type of cloth and finish employed. This Piper Colt was turned out by the Chickasha (OK) Flying Service.

Overspray does not carry great distances, therefore less masking is required. The fire hazard is zero; and there are no toxic fumes.

Always test masking tape with 7640 paint before use. Emulsion type paints will frequently bleed under, or soften, conventional crepe-back tapes. Film back, and flat-back waterproof tapes are superior. There is a difference between brands.

Eonnex 7640 paint may be re-coated as soon as it is dry to the touch. It may be wet-sanded when it is through-dried to the extent that it cannot be scraped off or lifted off by your fingernail. This paint should also be allowed to dry thoroughly (preferably overnight) before applying 7630 urethane enamel to insure that it is free of moisture that would react with the urethane. This emulsion paint may also be over-coated with clear butyrate dope. However, this is not a very durable finish. Urethane finish should be applied when the temperature is 70 degrees F or higher, low temperatures substantially lengthen drying time.

Cement Application: Applicator pads in the regular handle may be used to apply Eonnex 7602 and 7603 to large areas. The pads may be cut to exact size and stapled or tacked to a block of wood to apply cement the same width as the tapes. This is much faster than brushing and produces a better appearance. Pads used for 7602 may be washed and re-used. Pads used for 7603 must be discarded.

Eonnex 7605 four-ounce fabric, finished in 7640 and 7630 materials as recommended above, will weigh eight ounces per square yard and possess a minimum breaking strength of 125 pounds per inch width.

Eonnex 7606 three-ounce fabric, similarly finished, will weigh six and a-half ounces per square yard and have a minimum breaking strength of 100 pounds per inch width.

The Eonnex 7600 Manual contains additional data pertaining to the use of aircraft finishes.

Index